CHARLES DARWIN

Sarah R. Riedman

Introduction by
Professor Bert James Loewenberg

Henry Holt and Company   New York

FIRST EDITION

LIBRARY OF CONGRESS CATALOG CARD NUMBER: 59-7570

97448–0119

PRINTED IN THE UNITED STATES OF AMERICA

Acknowledgments

HOWEVER IMPRESSIVE the list of persons who have written about Darwin and Darwinism to whom the author is most grateful, she, like they must acknowledge their debt mainly to Darwin's own writing. For it's Darwin's books, his letters and autobiography that give the best account of his life and ideas. The best known of his works are, of course, *The Voyage of the Beagle, The Origin of Species,* and *The Descent of Man.*

Thanks also to his distinguished descendants, we have *The Life and Letters of Charles Darwin,* edited by his son Francis; his diary, notebooks, letters written on the voyage; and most recently his autobiography "with original omissions restored" edited by his granddaughter, Nora Barlow; and *Emma Darwin, A Century of Family Letters,* edited by his daughter, Henrietta Litchfield.

Especially, however, the author wishes to express her deep appreciation to Professor Bert James Loewenberg of Sarah Lawrence College. Second only to the satisfaction of writing the book itself, is the one of having earned the friendship of this warmly devoted Darwinian. My special gratitude goes to him for his inspiration, encouragement, and laborious plowing through the manuscript. Such flaws of errors it may contain are solely mine.

S.R.R.

Darwin Today

A NEW ERA in the history of thought began with the publication of *The Origin of Species* in 1859. While the idea of evolution is as old as human speculation, it was the great contribution of Charles Darwin to demonstrate and to confirm it. Charles Darwin did not invent the idea of evolution. Charles Darwin provided the evidence that made it possible for men to accept it.

Darwin demonstrated that individual plants and animals developed by natural means from previously existing plants and animals. Darwin did not seek to unravel the problem of the origin of life. He did not even seek to explain how species initially came into being. Given life and given the varieties of life in existence, Darwin sought to account for the changes in the forms of life: varieties to species, and species to varieties. This more limited purpose is suggested by the full title of his most famous book, *On the Origin of Species by Means of Natural Selection, or the Preservation of Favoured Races in the Struggle of Life*. Darwin's version of the concept of evolution infused naturalists with a new and invigorating zest. And from Darwin's day to our own, the concept of evolution has dominated biological thought.

Darwin presented a series of particular ideas to explain how the process of evolution worked. A century of biological exploration has widened our understanding of evolutionary methods. To mention but one example; newer scientific facts have changed our ideas about heredity, the vital key to the evolutionary process, the inheritance of similarities which accounts in part for the stability of a species, and the inheritance of differences which accounts in part for change.

5

Many Darwinian notions have been revised by the advance of research. Many novel views have replaced original Darwinian insights. Scholarship in biology and related fields has produced a staggering amount of data of which Darwin was unaware. Modern scholars in numerous areas of learning—philosophers, chemists, historians, sociologists as well as specialists in the zoological sciences—have evolved fresh interpretations unknown to Darwin.

The revolution inspired by Charles Darwin was not confined to plants and animals. Darwin extended the application of evolution to all forms of existence including man. After Darwin, man came to be viewed as an inseparable part of nature, an organic element within the evolutionary cycle. If man was one with nature, it followed that human attributes—mind, morals, values—had to be understood in new and different perspectives. It was not simply a revolution in biology, but a revolutionary change in man's image of himself and his works.

Charles Darwin gave his name to an era. Alfred Russel Wallace, co-discoverer of the principle of natural selection, shared public honors with his far more famous colleague, but the years from the mid-nineteenth to the twentieth century were the years of Charles Darwin. The Darwinian theory remains synonymous in the popular mind with the general theory of evolution.

The *Origin of Species* is a hundred years old. Scholars from all over the world are uniting to pay tribute to Darwin's character and to Darwin's achievement. Three anniversaries are to be commemorated: the voyage of the *Beagle* commenced in 1831, the presentation of the Linnean Society papers in which Darwin and Wallace first announced the theory of natural selection in 1858, and the appearance of the *Origin of Species* in 1859.

Colleges and universities, scientific and learned societies in the United States and abroad have arranged for meetings, symposiums, and expeditions. The Royal Society has designated a committee to administer a "Commonwealth Scientific Expedition" to commemorate Darwin's scientific expedition to South America. An expedition will sail to southern Chile. The Darwin Anniversary Committee, contemplates an overland scientific expedition to survey evolutionary changes in some of the lands visited by Darwin. In addition individual societies are designing their own programs of meetings and sponsoring books, papers and exhibits.

The Darwin Anniversary Committee like its counterparts is international in purpose and scope. Scholars represent the world, and the Darwin Anniversary Committee is composed of scientists from many countries. Darwins, Wedgwoods, and Huxleys appear on several boards and many programs, for there could not properly be Darwin celebrations without the descendants of Charles Darwin, Josiah Wedgwood and Thomas Henry Huxley. Lady Barlow, Darwin's granddaughter and herself a well-known historian of Darwin, is associated with Sir Julian Huxley, grandson of T. H. Huxley, as honorary co-chairman of the Darwin Anniversary Committee.

But the chief name on every roster and the chief purpose of every committee is Charles Darwin himself. And the men and women serving on these committees are eager not only to proclaim their obligation to a great idea, but to profess their admiration for the virtues of a great man.

BERT JAMES LOEWENBERG
Chairman, *Darwin Anniversary Committee*
Professor of History, *Sarah Lawrence College*

Bronxville, New York

Contents

Darwins and Wedgwoods 13
Schoolboy 22
At Loose Ends 29
Prelude to Adventure 38
Anchors Aweigh 48
University at Sea 56
Brazilian Forest to Argentine Pampas 65
Tierra del Fuego 78
Patagonia 88
Earthquakes and Volcanoes 94
Islands of the Giant Tortoise 105
A Naturalist's Cargo 117
Down House 134
The Amazing Coincidence 148
Masterpiece 159
The Long Harvest 174
Index 189

CHARLES DARWIN

I

Darwins and Wedgwoods

UNDER ITS GLASS CASE the gilt clock on the study mantel
was ticking away the morning of August 30, 1831. Time
had suddenly become important to the tall young man
waiting there and he felt the minute hand was moving too
slowly. It was the count down before the greatest decision
of his life.

Charles Darwin would not make the decision; that was
left to his wise and beloved father, who always knew the
right course to follow in treating his patients, or bringing
up his motherless children. Charles was now twenty-two,
but his father was still making up his mind for him. In a few
minutes, he would come in to announce what, after sleeping
on the question of the *Beagle* voyage, he thought his son
should do.

There had been other memorable conferences in this
room when Dr. Darwin had sternly rehearsed his son's
symptoms of chronic failure, and prescribed a new regi-
men. Charles had obediently swallowed his medicine and

promised to do better in preparing for a career. But what career? Charles had already prepared for two. He had backed out of medicine and was about to back out of the ministry. Only temporarily, of course, and only if his father consented.

With all his heart, he hoped his father would allow him to accept the astonishing offer which had come the night before, to sail as naturalist on a scientific voyage around the world. One of his Cambridge professors was behind this miracle for Charles was merely an amateur, leisure-time naturalist, and his only real qualification for the post on H.M.S. *Beagle* was the fact that he wanted it more than anyone else could possibly have done. This in itself was highly important; for the first time in his life Charles Darwin saw an opportunity to satisfy his vast curiosity about the world.

Dr. Robert Darwin came into the study with the vigorous step of a man who is huge without being ponderous. He weighed, in fact, well over 300 pounds and sometimes every ounce of it seemed to land on Charles. Reasonably and shrewdly, he pointed out that Charles was once more trying to run away from any serious effort to make something of himself. He described the discomforts and dangers of a long voyage and somehow managed to make it look like a harebrained, ridiculous undertaking. In short, the answer was no.

Thoroughly crushed by his father's words, Charles gave up his dream of Teneriffe and Tierra del Fuego. It never occurred to him that his father might change his mind.

The story of Charles Darwin began with the close friendship between his grandfathers, Erasmus Darwin and Josiah Wedgwood, who first met as doctor and patient when they were in their early thirties. Young Dr. Darwin, trained at Edinburgh and Cambridge, had just begun his practice in

Lichfield in Staffordshire, but he was such a remarkable person that he had already made an impression in the neighborhood. However, it was odd that he should be called to treat an obscure young potter who lived thirty miles away. Plainly, fate was at work.

Josiah Wedgwood had left school at nine to work as apprentice in his brother's pottery, which was merely one room in the family cottage. He had been lame since he was twelve; but few men could run toward fame and fortune as rapidly as Josiah could limp. Just now he was starting out as an independent potter and he hoped that Dr. Darwin could do something about his ailing right knee.

There was little that a physician could do about the knee. But Erasmus had an infallible instinct for exceptional people and he recognized the singular gifts in Josiah. They became friends and, side by side, they became famous.

Josiah became famous for one thing; the creation of the beautiful ware that still carries his name around the world. He presented a tea service to Queen Charlotte and earned the title of Royal Potter. From the Empress Catherine of Russia to colonial hostesses in Philadelphia, Wedgwood was in demand.

Dr. Darwin, delighted with the classical grace of his friend's designs, suggested that he name his pottery Etruria after the ancient civilization in Italy. The Etruria Works and Staffordshire, almost interchangeable terms, became famous in an amazingly short time.

Erasmus Darwin's fame was built up more slowly, out of numerous elements. He stood so high in his profession that he was invited to become royal physician to King George III. He declined, not wishing to move all the way to London and not liking the king's bullying of the American colonies. A mountain of a man, he stayed in Lichfield and let patients come to him, as they gladly did, from every corner of England and often from the rest of Europe.

Darwin possessed tremendous vitality and lived several lives at once. Living just at the beginnings of the age of power, he was interested in steam and electricity. He helped his friend Matthew Boulton struggle to perfect the steam engine and nearly went into partnership with him before James Watt came along. The Boulton-Watt combination succeeded in producing the steam engine which transformed the world, with Erasmus cheering them every step of the way. He predicted the submarine and the airplane and devised a talking machine, a canal lock, and a rotary pump, along with a host of electrical devices.

As time went on, Erasmus Darwin turned to botanical studies, rather whimsically publishing his observations in the form of verses which enjoyed popularity in his own day. His final work, *Zoonomia,* was a different matter. It contained the germ of the evolutionary theory which his grandson was to work out in his own very different way.

It might seem that Erasmus, who corresponded with Benjamin Franklin and Rousseau, who was a great intellectual in his own right, would have little in common with Josiah Wedgwood, the rather quiet potter who had left school at nine. They had a great deal in common, if only because Dr. Darwin swept his friend into his own whirlwind of interests and into the little circle of remarkable men he had gathered around him.

Wedgwood was a frequent guest at the monthly dinners of the Lunar Society, held at the full moon so that the members could ride home comfortably. They called themselves "Lunatics," but it was a notable group, with Erasmus the presiding genius, like Dr. Samuel Johnson with *his* little circle on the other side of England. There were, in the Lunar Society, Boulton and Watt, Joseph Priestley, the discoverer of oxygen, and Dr. William Small, to begin the list. Dr. Small had been Thomas Jefferson's teacher at William and Mary College in Virginia and, as Jefferson said of his beloved friend, had "probably fixed the destinies of my life" by opening up the wonders of science "and of the system of things in which we are placed"—by which Jefferson meant man in society.

Over long dinners, the Lunatics joked and argued and threshed out an endless variety of subjects—science and inventions, the Stamp Act, politics, literature, Wedgwood's campaign for better roads and for canals, and Darwin's crusade for pure water and sewage disposal. They were all Whigs, champions of the American patriots who were struggling against King George and his Tory ministers. The dining club was started about ten years before this struggle flamed into the American Revolution and all through the great upheaval its members were cheering for the American side.

The Darwin-Wedgwood friendship was firmly based in shared convictions and ideals. They agreed in their hatred of slavery, Wedgwood designed a medallion showing a black slave kneeling in chains, with the inscription, "Am I not a man and a brother?" As they prospered and acquired families, their friendship deepened into a close affection which radiated to their children. The doctor's son, Robert began a lifelong friendship with young Josiah, the Wedgwood heir. The affinity between the families was so complete that gentle little Susannah Wedgwood and Dr. Darwin idolized each other like father and daughter. When she came to visit the Darwins, Susannah gravely attempted to teach the doctor piano. This huge, clumsy man with his pitted face and bulbous nose charmed everybody who knew him and his effect on females of all ages was magic.

There was a period when the Darwin and Wedgwood boys were not quite ready for college, and the two families were pooled in an experimental school. It was established at the Wedgwood home, Etruria Hall, under Josiah's close supervision. In that day, and for a long time to come, English schools concentrated on Greek and Latin, ignoring such "foibles" as science and living languages. But at the delightful Wedgwood house, a chemist and a French tutor presided over the classroom periods and corporal punishment was banned. The children called themselves "Darwinians and Etrurians" and got along famously.

Robert Darwin chose his father's profession. After he finished his medical training at Edinburgh and Leyden, he began practice in Shrewsbury, a thriving town in Shropshire about twenty miles from Etruria Hall and an equal distance from the lovely Susannah. They were married a year after Josiah Wedgwood died. A great friendship was ended, but the Darwin-Wedgwood clan was now established.

Charles Robert Darwin, the fifth child of this happy marriage, was born on February 12, 1809, the day Abraham Lincoln was born. In that "miracle year" of 1809, a number of promising infants made their appearance: Tennyson, Poe and Oliver Wendell Holmes, Mendelssohn and Chopin, Gladstone and Braille.

Since one of the outstanding traits of the Darwin-Wedgwood clan was warm family affection, the people important to Charles all lived inside the big red brick house called the Mount. There were his brother Erasmus, five years older; his sisters Susan, Caroline and Marianne, ranging from six to eleven years his senior; and his little sister Catherine, born the year after his advent. The girls promised to become beauties like their mother, and the boys to inherit the Darwin stature without the bulk and the full round Darwin brow without their grandfather's unfortunate nose. Even their father had managed to escape the nose.

Robert Darwin was a man of force, practical benevolence, and considerable charm. Robert was not great, but he was effective, very successful as a physician, and extremely kind to the poor. He was in fact a philanthropist, devoting much time and money to the Shrewsbury slum, Frankwell, treating the sick, establishing a school for little children, and opening his purse without stint. He could well afford this, for his private practice brought him a large income and Susannah had inherited 25,000 pounds, a large fortune for that time.

The good doctor had one gift which Charles too possessed —a remarkable talent for close observation. In his father this was developed as a keen insight into people. His patients declared that he was a mind reader and Charles grew up with the conviction that his father could divine the most secret recesses of his soul. As a tiny boy he had committed some small mischief that he was sure nobody had seen and yet the moment his father came into the room he demanded, "Now you've done something naughty, Charles. What was it?" On a more agreeable level, Charles enjoyed rides in his father's yellow chaise, for the doctor would point out every bird and darting rabbit along the country lanes. Charles was not far behind in developing the all-seeing eye which gave them both much pleasure and much to think about.

He was an extremely gentle little boy and a painfully shy one. For some reason, he remembered very little of his early childhood and almost nothing of his mother, who died when he was eight. The lovely feel of her velvet dress, the delightful colored silks in her workbox—these were safe memories to keep because they were not too close to the dear lost mother.

But he could remember when he and Catherine were toddlers, learning their letters at his sister Caroline's knee, with his little sister much quicker than he was at lessons. He felt Caroline was too strict and too much like their father in suspecting trouble. He could not come into a room where she was without asking himself, "What will she blame me for now?"

Charles was an unusually sensitive child. Once he beat a puppy and he mourned the crime till his dying day. It is normal for a small boy to be cruel at least once and forget it. Charles could not, through a long lifetime of loving and being loved by dogs.

When he was put into an infant school, his extreme diffidence drove him into a period of telling whoppers to impress the other children. He announced that his mother had taught him a secret way to tell the name of a flower—it was written inside, if you knew where to look. He claimed that he could make polyanthuses and primroses any color he liked by watering them with colored fluids.

These harmless fibs were connected with his mother, who was still, despite growing ill-health, working in her flower beds and greenhouse and feeding her beautiful tame pigeons. The gardens were the best part of the Mount, for the house itself was square, substantial, facing abruptly on the street. Dr. Darwin had chosen to build his house in an unfashionable part of town near the poor folk of Frankwell but he had taken care to include the Severn River in his plans.

Shrewsbury, the county seat of Shropshire, was near the Welsh border and an ancient ruined castle recalled the days of the bloody border wars. The Severn made almost a complete circle around the town and the Mount was built on one of its high banks. In reality, the house turned not on the street but on its lawns and orchards leading down to the river, with a view of woods and pastures beyond.

Here Dr. Darwin was blissfully happy for he had a green thumb, and fruit trees, flowers, shrubs, flourished under his care. In this enclosed place he could see nothing but peace and beauty. Shrewsbury, with its smug, provincial Tories whose fees were making him rich, was invisible. Frankwell, and its incessant crises of poverty and sickness was far away. The doctor had his troubles, for the sight of blood always upset him and the Shrewsbury Infirmary was a busy place. He was getting so enormous that he dared not climb the rickety stairs of old run-down houses without sending his coachman ahead to make sure they would bear his weight.

While the doctor was attending to his practice, his youngest children were stowed safely away, for this was a Don't Touch garden. Charles and Catherine, each with a private branch of a huge Spanish chestnut for perch, looked down at their father in his big garden hat as he moved from flowering quince to a young pear tree refusing to flower, reproving it in the tiny voice that always surprised them.

Their mother was not busy among her flowers any longer and after a while they knew better than to expect, as children will, that some day she would come back.

2

Schoolboy

WHEN HE WAS NINE, Charles entered the Shrewsbury Grammar School, where his brother Erasmus had been a pupil for three years. It was only a mile from the Mount, but the brothers lived at the school; that was a necessary part of a young gentleman's education. Shrewsbury was a famous old school founded nearly three centuries before and now recovering from a long slump under the firm hand of the headmaster, Dr. Samuel Butler.

Dr. Butler was considered ideal. He was pompous, literal-minded, a walking encyclopedia of mostly useless knowledge. His system of discipline combined bribery in the form of "merit money" for good work and the birch rod for mischief. Faithful to tradition, his school taught virtually nothing but Greek and Latin. "While your son remains here," he told parents, "he will always be exercised in Latin and Greek composition both in prose and verse and the higher he gets in school the more he will have of it."

For seven years, Charles was given more than he wanted

of the classics, with a smattering of ancient history and geography. He so resisted this cramming with dead languages that a few years later, when he really wanted to know Greek, he had to learn the alphabet all over again. There was no science, no mathematics, no modern languages. Even as an old man he was bitter about those years. "Nothing could have been worse for the development of my mind than Dr. Butler's school," he wrote in his Autobiography. "The school as a means of education to me was simply a blank."

He kept his mind as blank as possible. Every day he memorized forty or fifty lines from the poems of Homer or Virgil, a last minute chore during morning chapel, and would remember them just long enough to recite them in class. A poor speller with no gift for languages and less for versifying, he produced the required compositions only because his schoolmates helped him out.

Dr. Darwin was deeply disappointed that his son dragged along toward the bottom of his class. He did not suspect— and neither did Charles for a long time—that a first-class mind was being smothered under the outlandish school system of that day. Charles needed the sort of training that did not even exist then and his education could only begin when he himself took charge of it. So he went through the seven years at Shrewsbury with his mind wool-gathering, a sturdy, friendly, commonplace boy, regarded as none too bright.

Since young minds must have some nourishment, Charles fed on what snacks were available. The odes of Horace with their charming pictures of country life, Thomson's *Seasons*, the poems of Byron and Scott, were better fare than he found in the classroom and Shakespeare put iron in his blood. A schoolmate lent him *Wonders of the World* and he read it over and over, dreaming of travel in strange and distant lands.

He filled out his schooling at random. A private tutor taught him geometry, which he found most satisfying. His uncle showed him how to use the vernier, a movable scale for reading the barometer. Erasmus, a beloved companion at school, left to take his medical training at Cambridge and Edinburgh but continued to encourage Charles' private reading. On vacations the brothers carried on a most delightful project. They turned a toolhouse in the Mount garden into a laboratory where they performed chemical experiments. Erasmus did most of the work, learning how to make compounds and discharge gases. Charles was his helper and read several chemistry books as the work progressed. Of course their father and Dr. Butler considered this a complete waste of time and at school Charles was nicknamed "Gas." He took his schoolmates' teasing good-naturedly, for this shy, solitary boy had a great gift for happy relations with others. Those in authority—the headmaster, Dr. Darwin, and sometimes his older sister Caroline —might paralyze him, but he was a warm and friendly soul, like most of the Darwin-Wedgwood clan.

In the rough-and-tumble of dormitory life, Charles held his own. Even the bullies were kept in place by knowing that Charles, taller and more powerfully built than anybody his age, could beat them if he chose. With his athlete's build, he might have shone in school sports but he had too much else to do.

He was now collecting stones and insects in a fairly systematic way. On a summer visit to the coast of Wales, he was able to distinguish varieties of insects very slightly different from those he knew in Shrewsbury. Walking along the beach, he enjoyed watching the gulls and cormorants straggling home at sunset after a day's fishing. He became fascinated with birds, learning their habits in long country rambles and reading what came to hand about them.

What took him away from school most often was the

Mount, which he could reach in a few moments of earnest running. There were all the familiar delights: the dogs and horses and jovial stable hands, in the kitchen an indulgent cook with goodies she had put by for him, in the drawing-room his pretty sisters, waiting for the tide to come in. The "tide" was their father, home from a round of patients, rich and poor. He would settle his enormous frame into an easy chair and for two hours deliver a running discourse on the events of the day, along with the lessons to be drawn from these experiences and moral precepts which he hoped his children would take to heart. Since he found the world full of interesting things, this nightly lecture had its value and the children were resigned to it. But visitors were appalled by the ritual and Aunt Elizabeth Wedgwood, the soul of kindness, described it as "stiff and awful."

At the Wedgwood house twenty miles away, there were no parental lectures, no pressures on anybody. The beautiful house and grounds of Maer overflowed with the eight small Wedgwoods, their Darwin cousins, and various relatives and friends, all doing exactly as they pleased. This remarkable atmosphere of freedom stemmed from gay and gracious Aunt Elizabeth, one of the most enchanting women of her day. Uncle Josiah thoroughly approved of freedom, but he himself was a rather reserved and silent man. The Darwin girls stood in awe of Uncle Jos and were astonished that Charles talked freely to him, as if he were "a common mortal." But Charles was always his uncle's favorite and the two had the greatest respect and affection for each other. Uncle Jos, in fact, had a growing suspicion that Charles was going to amount to something. Perhaps nobody in the family helped him more in the difficult job of growing up.

Dr. Darwin considered his brother-in-law one of the wisest men he ever knew and this tribute was justified. Josiah was making a huge success of the pottery works a few miles away. Like his father, he was a liberal who kept an open mind, encouraging others to express their opinions and never trying to impose his own views if he happened to disagree. To Charles this was a decided change from the system at home, where Papa was infallible.

As for Aunt Elizabeth, it never entered her lovely head to spoil the natural happiness of children. Her own childhood had been fantastic. Her father made his daughters learn the art of conversation by threatening them with a horsewhip. Oddly enough, the nine sisters made brilliant marriages and were famous for their witty and charming conversation. And Elizabeth, for one, was every child's good fairy.

Her magic made Maer a perfect place for children. The great stone Tudor house with high ceilings and spacious oak-paneled rooms had been given bay windows and a wide portico to enlarge the view of the gardens sloping down to Lake Maer and the wooded hill enclosing its farther side. The famous landscape artist, Capability Brown, had worked his own spell on the grounds. He had the gift of planning gardens so that they never looked formally arranged.

The resources for amusement were endless. Following the sandy path around the lake was the simplest and the lake itself offered fishing, boating, sailing, and skating. The stables were full of riding horses; the woods full of birds and game for the shooting season, which soon became the high point of the year for Charles. There was a more or less continual house party at Maer, providing enough young people for games, dancing, and acting charades and plays. And no one minded if a boy felt like sitting alone beside the lake to listen to the evening songs of the waterfowl, instead of joining the group on the portico steps, deep in some discussion about books or politics.

When Caroline and Susan Darwin were at Maer, there were sure to be what their cousin Emma called "wicked times" and "revels," by which she meant dances and flirtations and mad rushing up and down stairs to assemble costumes and props for the next play. Of Charles' four sisters, these were the lively ones, even at home. He saw little of his oldest sister Marianne, who married and moved away while he was still at school and his younger sister Catherine was a quiet soul. But the two middle sisters were tall, beautiful, and full of high spirits. Lovely Susan was her father's favorite. She could turn some little misadventure with a tipsy coachman or a broken carriage pole into a comic recital that sent him into roars of laughter. Caroline's more formal manner and proud airs earned her the nickname of "Duchess." Aunt Elizabeth had platoons of nieces, but of them all, Caroline was her favorite.

When the "wicked times" were at their height, the house could be pandemonium and even Aunt Elizabeth could write one of her sisters that "a little calm will be very agreeable." But she remained, as a friend remarked, "the gentlest mistress in England having the noisiest household" and never tried to restrain the fun. She loved fun herself.

Under all the gaiety the Wedgwoods were giving the young people under their roof something priceless; the liberation of minds from the prejudices and false notions that harden into a mental plaster cast and prevent the mind from growing. A young guest at Maer wrote in her diary as good a description as one could find of the Wedgwood home. It is reported in the letters of Emma Darwin.

> I never saw anything pleasanter than the ways of this family, and one reason is the freedom of speech upon every subject; there is no difference in politics or principles of any kind that makes it treason to speak one's mind openly, and they all do it. . . . They have freedom in their actions in this house as well as in their principles. Doors and windows stand open, you are nowhere in confinement. You may do as you like; you

are surrounded by books and all look most tempting to read. . . . All this sounds and is delightful.

While the Mount could never compare with Maer, there were frequent parties there for the Wedgwoods and Sarah and Fanny Owen, friends who lived nearby. One winter they all took singing lessons from Mr. Sor, music teacher to the elite of Shrewsbury. They enjoyed these sessions, for Mr. Sor made them entertaining on purpose—and sometimes inadvertently, when he sat down at the piano and sang solos so thunderously that his face got purple and his vocal cords, they suspected, were reduced to shreds. Charles was the dunce here, as he was at school. He was tone deaf and could never carry a tune. He could not even recognize a tune unless it had a very marked rhythm.

However, Charles was always glad to be with the Owen girls, even during the torments of music. One great bond with Sarah and Fanny was their love of hunting; and the fact that there was shooting available at their place, Woodhouse, made him a frequent guest there during the season.

For Charles could boast one accomplishment, he was a dead shot. When he was about fifteen he visited a relative who lived near Birmingham and was taken shooting. Charles never forgot the excitement of bringing down his first snipe; his hands trembled so that he couldn't reload his gun. After that he practiced until he became a crack marksman. Indoors, he would work in front of a mirror to perfect his style. Loading his gun with a cap, he would fire at a lighted candle and put it out.

"I do not believe anyone could have shown more zeal for the most holy cause than I did for shooting birds," he wrote long afterwards.

All very well—but at school his grades were still dismal.

3

At Loose Ends

DR. DARWIN seldom lost his temper but the day came when he stormed at Charles, "You care for nothing but shooting, dogs, and rat catching and you will be a disgrace to yourself and all your family."

Charles was most unhappy at this outburst. He had done so badly at his studies that his father was taking him out of school at sixteen, two years short of the usual term. This reprieve was welcome, but Charles was deeply ashamed. He had failed at his school work and failed to please his father, which was far more important to him.

Perhaps Dr. Darwin's private reason for taking his son out of school was a shrewd suspicion that Dr. Butler was not the right man to cope with the problem of young Charles Darwin. Charles was a puzzle. Here was a boy who seemed to possess at least average intelligence, but who was stubbornly dull in the classroom. What *was* Charles Darwin? What did he propose to make of himself? What did he care about besides dogs and guns?

If Charles had had the slightest idea of his own potential, he could have answered, "everything. I care about everything around me, stones and plants, insects and birds, and fish. I'd like to know every last thing about every sort of animal and plant on earth. But they don't teach these things in school."

This tremendous curiosity about the natural world drove Charles to little piecemeal attempts to find out the truth, the whole truth. But he did not suspect how rare this sort of curiosity is.

The stowaway scientist deep in Charles' mind was fascinated by the Shrewsbury Bell Stone. This enormous rock was plainly an intruder in Shropshire; it must have come from somewhere else. But how? What unknown power had brought it here? An old Shropshire man, who knew something of rocks and was the first to point out the huge boulder to Charles, told him there were no others like it nearer than Cumberland or Scotland. He solemnly assured the boy that the world would come to an end long before anybody found out how the Bell Stone had been moved to Shrewsbury. Charles was deeply impressed but he felt that somewhere, somehow, this mystery was going to be explained. And it was, years later, when the Swiss-American, Louis Agassiz astonished the world with his discovery that successive ice-ages had rolled glaciers over the continents, making titanic changes in the scenery and deposited the huge stone in Shrewsbury. Charles was immensely relieved.

Meanwhile at sixteen, he must choose a career. He could not, so his father chose for him. Charles might as well go into the family profession and study medicine. Erasmus had finished three years at Cambridge and in the fall of 1825 would enroll at Edinburgh University to complete his medical training. Charles might as well go to Edinburgh with his brother.

This "might as well" attitude reflected the faint hopes of

father and son that Charles would at last get interested in something worthwhile. He spent the summer as his father's apprentice in treating the charity patients. He visited them, wrote down their symptoms, and reported the cases as fully as possible. Dr. Darwin would then write prescriptions, and Charles would make up the medicines and deliver them to the patients. Doctors were their own pharmacists in those days. Charles was glad he had done a little chemistry in the toolhouse. On the whole, the summer was a success. The humble folk of Frankwell responded to the boy's gentle and sympathetic manner. Dr. Darwin was genuinely pleased and sent his sons off to Edinburgh with assurances that one day they would add lustre to the already famous Darwin name —if they worked hard.

Edinburgh saw to that. Classes began at eight and went on all day, six days a week. The grey old Scots city was given to tall, uncomfortable buildings and the brothers had to climb four flights of stairs to get to their living quarters. Erasmus, Robert, and now the third generation of Darwins were learning the noblest of all professions in the most vener- ated medical school in the British Isles. Their uncle Charles was buried here, in the family vault of Dr. Andrew Duncan. That brilliant Charles who had been stricken with smallpox in the midst of his medical studies.

There was an aura of greatness about the university, but was it past greatness? Dr. Duncan was still lecturing on materia medica, but Charles wrote Caroline that those lec- tures were "something fearful to remember."

In 1754, Erasmus had learned his anatomy from Dr. Monro, whose lectures were now read aloud by his grandson, word for word. Had no progress been made in anatomy in the last seventy-one years? Charles did not, as some of the stu- dents did, pelt the droning old man with dried peas. But he wrote his sister, "I dislike him and his lectures so much that I cannot speak with decency about them."

Erasmus and Charles soon cut all but the required classes and worked in the library, where it was possible to learn something. Most of the students took private lessons in dissection outside the university, but Charles was too squeamish to face the dreaded dissecting room. He was sorry later on, that he missed training in dissection and in drawing.

Twice he went to watch surgery in the hospital theater. Anesthetics were still in the future and an operation was a terrible thing to witness. The second was on a child, and Charles rushed out of the room before it was finished. Nothing on earth could induce him to go through this nightmare again.

He did make the rounds of the hospital wards quite faithfully. But somehow visiting patients in Edinburgh was very different from his summer's work at home. There he had had a personal interest in his patients, and he had been proud of the responsibility. He missed his father's wisdom and joy in work—there was a born doctor! Erasmus was the best possible brother, but Erasmus was bored and homesick, too.

Summer brought escape and the familiar happiness of home. And yet the Mount was only a base now for explorations farther afield. With two friends, Charles spent a month tramping through North Wales, walking thirty miles a day and sleeping under the stars. As a final fling, they climbed Mount Snowdon. Then he took one of his sisters for a horseback tour of the mountains and by late August was ready for the shooting at Maer and Woodhouse.

My zeal was so great that I used to place my shooting boots open by my bed-side when I went to bed, so as not to lose half a minute in putting them on in the morning [he wrote in his *Autobiography*]. How I did enjoy shooting! But I think that I must have been half-consciously ashamed of my zeal, for I tried to persuade myself that shooting was almost an intellectual employment; it required so much skill to judge where to find most game and to hunt the dogs well.

Charles went back to Edinburgh alone, for Erasmus had finished his training. In reality, Charles had also dropped everything but the appearance of being a medical student. He was, unknowingly, acting like a budding scientist. He acquired new friends; a botanist, a zoologist, a geologist, and a museum curator who collected shells. It was the young zoologist, Dr. Robert Edmund Grant, who was most important at this stage of Charles' uncertain career. They were walking once by the tidal pools of the River Forth when Grant suddenly began talking about the French biologist, Jean Baptiste Lamarck, whose ideas about evolution he greatly admired. Grant enthusiastically described Lamarck's theories on the development of new species.

Charles was dumbfounded. These ideas were familiar to him; he had found much the same line of thought in his grandfather's *Zoonomia*, which he and his sisters had read not long before. It had never occurred to him that his grandfather had originated a theory promising enough to set later scientists to work. He had read *Zoonomia* without understanding it, without finding the dazzling speculation it contained about how life begins and changes. He was still too ignorant to know where Erasmus Darwin's thinking left off and Lamarck's began, or whether they were right or wrong. But he had had an extremely interesting reaction to *Zoonomia*. It had disappointed him because his grandfather had come plump out with a theory, not bothering to bolster it with facts. And Charles, by a sort of instinct, worked just the opposite way, from facts and observation and later from experiment, which some day might pile up into a theory explaining everything.

Just now his work was with the tiny creatures at the edge

of the sea. With Grant and John Coldstream, who was studying marine zoology, he haunted the tidal pools, collecting
specimens and dissecting them as well as he could. He made
friends with the Newhaven oystermen, who took him along
on their fishing trips to new spots along the coast. Back in
his rooms, he would study the day's catch. With a poor microscope and no skill at dissection, his results were often
disappointing. But his eagerness to find things out for himself led to some interesting discoveries.

Not satisfied with Dr. Grant's explanation that some small
brown structures they found floating on the water were
seeds, Charles studied them carefully under his microscope.
To his amazement, he saw tiny bodies emerge from the
"seeds" and swim on their own by moving their oar-like cilia.
They were in fact larvae of the sea mat *Flustra* and not seeds
at all.

Later, he discovered that little round bodies, supposed to
be the young state of a seaweed, were really the egg cases
of the skate leech.

He read short reports on his two little discoveries before
the Plinian Society, a group of students who met once a week
to discuss natural science. He joined the Plinian and also the
revered Royal Medical Society, which he found more ad-
dicted to talking rubbish than the student group. Dr. Grant
took him to meetings of the Wernerian Society, devoted to
natural history and here, in December 1826, he heard John
James Audubon lecture and demonstrate on the platform
how he arranged freshly-killed birds in natural positions as
models for his incomparable drawings. Audubon was spending the winter in Edinburgh, where his great work, *The
Birds of America,* was being printed and four hundred of
his original drawings were on exhibition at the Royal Society.

One would think this feast was specially designed for

Charles Darwin, but he was not quite ready for such rich fare. He was taking lessons in taxidermy.

At this period Charles sometimes let personalities stand in the way of things he wanted and needed to know. Far too sensitive to people, he was put off by Audubon's vanity and flamboyance, missing his genius and his vast knowledge of the birds and mammals of the New World. In the same way, he was so bored by Dr. Robert Jameson, "that old brown dry stick" who lectured on geology, that he turned his back on the whole subject. He determined "never as long as I lived to read a book on Geology, or in any way to study the science."

Fortunately, he was to change his mind about geology. His dead set against Jameson's method of teaching was justified. He tells the following story in his autobiography.

On a field trip, Dr. Jameson and his class were inspecting a *dike*, which as every geologist knows now, is an intrusion of molten lava filling a crack in an older rock. As the students gathered around the spot, the professor pointed to the crack and the black rock filling the seam.

"What do you suppose happened here?" he asked, but did not wait for an answer.

Charles made a careful inspection. He could plainly see the uneven edges of the black substance which had flowed into every cranny branching off from the main crevice.

"This fissure has been filled in by sediment finding its way in from above," Dr. Jameson said with finality. He added with a sneer, "There are those who maintain that it has been injected from beneath in a molten condition."

How could anybody with eyes think of dribbles of sand explaining the *dike?* Volcanic rock was lying all around. Some of it, when it was spewed up from an underground cauldron, had flowed hot and molten into every crack and then had cooled down into black igneous rock. Charles was disgusted with a teacher who wouldn't look and find the answer to his questions from nature itself.

By the end of his second year at Edinburgh, Charles was sure he would never become a physician. Nothing in his studies had aroused his interest or suggested what he should adopt as a future career. The one incentive that keeps most people plugging along, the necessity of earning a living, had now vanished. He was told, perhaps by Erasmus, that he could count on inheriting enough money to give him a decent income. Younger sons were not always so fortunate. But in the case of Charles, who apparently lacked ambition, the assurance that he could get along for the rest of his life without having to earn a living set him really adrift.

Naturally he dreaded the next sham battle with his father, in which Charles would make a few futile gestures with a wooden sword and Dr. Darwin would bring up his heavy artillery. Luck was often with Charles and he was able to spend most of the spring vacation far from the Mount. Caroline joined him in London and then Uncle Jos took them both to Switzerland, where Fanny and Emma Wedgwood had been visiting an aunt. Brief glimpses of Geneva and Paris were all Charles was ever to enjoy of continental Europe.

He finished his last term at Edinburgh and then there was no escape. He went home to face his father. Once more Dr. Darwin, after expressing his pain and anger over Charles' career at Edinburgh, demanded what he proposed to do. Once more Charles had no idea. It did not take his father long to suggest the only alternative. The careers open to young gentlemen were the army or navy, law, medicine, divinity. Military and legal traditions were lacking in the family and Charles had now repudiated medicine. Ergo, he must think about becoming a clergyman.

Startled, Charles begged for time to think this over. He

had, of course, to examine his conscience and be sure that he accepted all the dogmas of the Established Church. The Wedgwood side of the house was Unitarian and all the family was liberal, or perhaps vague, in matters of religion.

While Charles was dutifully reading the standard works on divinity to make sure what he believed, he had a delightful encounter at Maer with Sir James Mackintosh, who had married one of Aunt Elizabeth's sisters. The great statesman talked brilliantly of history, his special field; of politics, and moral philosophy. He was the "best converser" Charles had ever heard and perhaps Charles was the best listener Sir James had met. At any rate, he told one of the Wedgwoods, "There is something in that young man that interests me." This recognition by a distinguished man was a comfort and an inspiration to Charles for a long time to come.

By the summer's end he had settled any doubts about his orthodoxy and was beginning to think that life as a clergyman in some quiet country spot might not be too bad. Meanwhile, he would work for his divinity degree at Cambridge and this prospect was most agreeable. It was at this point that Charles discovered he had all but forgotten his Greek, so he stayed at the Mount cramming with a tutor, until the New Year of 1828.

4

Prelude to Adventure

IN THE AUTOBIOGRAPHY which Charles Darwin wrote for his family, he remembered his Cambridge years as "the most joyful in my happy life; for I was then in excellent health, and almost always in high spirits."

His happiness came from the companionship of his new friends, also in the highest spirits, and from the pleasures of collecting insects. Even more than at Edinburgh, his real life was outside the classroom. Until his third year, when he had to cram desperately to pass examinations for his B.A. degree, he managed to slide along with a minimum of work.

In those years he showed something of his grandfather Erasmus' joviality and delight in good fellowship. As a fine specimen of the Darwin-Wedgwood clan, he possessed great charm, warmth, generosity, and lively wit; all blending now with the gentleness and extreme modesty which marked him all his life. Robust and unusually tall, his face promised interesting possibilities; the amiable but resolute mouth and the steady gaze of his grey eyes under the dome of a forehead did not belong to a young man who was going to waste his life.

He did waste some time at Cambridge and did miss chances to learn, but it would be hard to find a college student innocent on that score. Dr. Darwin had sent Charles to Cambridge to save him from becoming an "idle sporting man," but he happened to enter Christ College, headquarters of the sporting set. From the senior tutor down, they all loved hunting, horses, dogs. Many of the students collected insects as a sort of competitive game. Naturally, Charles was completely at home with these other gay young sportsmen and collectors, who dutifully followed the unwritten law of Christ College banning overwork at studies.

With his boon companions of the Gourmet Club, Charles enjoyed long evenings of food and wine, cards and singing. They had riding horses and made expeditions afoot to find beetles or butterflies to swell their collections. Not all of them had a scientific interest in insects. They were simply racing each other to get the most specimens or the rarest ones and since this "bug-hunting" mania extended to the whole undergraduate body, there were many competitors. The rules of the game allowed buying specimens from each other or from townsmen who made a pretty penny collecting for students. Charles made friends with the Newhaven oystermen who invited him to travel with them and look for specimens. He much preferred to do his own hunting, with beetles a specialty.

I will give proof of my zeal [he wrote in his autobiography.] One day, on tearing off some old bark, I saw two rare bettles, and seized one in each hand; then I saw a third and new kind, which I could not bear to lose, so that I popped the one which I held in my right hand into my mouth. Alas! it ejected some intensely acrid fluid, which burnt my tongue so that I was forced to spit the beetle out, which was lost, as was the third one.

He was zealous at amassing treasures from under logs or the keels of river barges but he was not scientific. He did not look up his specimens in textbooks of entomology to find how they were classed and he did not dissect them. And yet his wonderful gift for observation enabled him to recognize and name every new species he found. For years he remembered the exact post, tree, or spot on the river bank where he had picked up a rare beetle. Some of his finds were rare enough to be published in a textbook. "No poet ever felt more delighted at seeing his first poem published than I did at seeing, in Stephen's *Illustrations of British Insects,* the magic words, 'captured by C. Darwin, Esq.'"

It happened that a second cousin, William Fox, was then at Cambridge in Charles' own college. He said later that it was Fox's fine collection of butterflies which started him insect hunting. More important, Fox introduced him to the botany professor, John Steven Henslow, who became the greatest influence of his college years and the force which launched him on his singular career.

Henslow was still in his early thirties, a most handsome man who was a favorite with the students. A good many of them would take his courses year after year, for his lectures and field trips fascinated them. Charles had first heard of Henslow from his brother, who declared that the botanist knew everything. Besides his own specialty, Henslow had a wide knowledge of chemistry, mineralogy, entomology, and other sciences. The fact that he was a Doctor of Divinity to boot had a special significance to Charles. He was impressed by Henslow's high moral qualities and his warm humanity.

Charles began to appear at the Friday evening meetings in Henslow's house, where professors, fellows, and students interested in many lines of natural history gathered for informal talks. Before long a special relationship developed between Charles and the older man, and they took almost daily walks together, often ending in dinner at the Henslow house. Charles became known at Cambridge as "the man who walks with Henslow." His new friend was not the only professor who saw unusual promise in the young student, often some scientist planning a solitary field trip would invite him to come along. Thus he picked up scraps of knowledge which he filed away in his mind, excellent for its memory.

During his first year or two at Cambridge his education in science was decidedly scrappy. The old prejudice against geology which had soured his Edinburgh days was still strong and kept him from attending the lectures of Adam Sedgwick, a real giant in this science. Despite tutors, he failed algebra and was not too successful in geometry, which he liked better. He took a botany course with Henslow, went on his field trips, and learned much in their long private talks.

He admired Henslow's method of drawing conclusions only after long, close observations. And he never forgot the supreme tact with which the Professor handled his early bungles in botany. One day when Charles was examining some pollen grains on a damp surface, he noted the thrusting out of the tubes and excitedly ran to tell Henslow of this marvel. It was, of course, merely the ABC of the process of plant fertilization but Henslow did not crack a smile. He agreed that the phenomenon was remarkable and then went on to explain the whole process of pollen fertilizing ovum to produce seed. This was so gracefully done that Charles was spared embarrassment. He was so extremely sensitive that a rebuff or a touch of ridicule might have put him "off" botany then and there.

During holidays there was a familiar pattern. Charles would go home to face the music, for despite the efforts of his sisters, especially Susan, to soften up their father in advance, Dr. Darwin was sure to give his younger son a trouncing. Charles was frivolous about preparing for the ministry, he was always exceeding his allowance in riotous living and so on and on. Then Charles would escape to Maer, where his cousins loved him, even if his "bug hunting" seemed rather excessive, and Uncle Jos remained his firm friend. In the hunting season, there were glorious days at Maer and at Woodhouse, with the Owen girls and their blustery father, who was extremely fond of Charles. He would make visits to some of his Cambridge friends and to London, where Erasmus was postponing a career as doctor. Erasmus managed to elude medicine all his life, but his great interest in all the arts gave Charles opportunities to enjoy painting, music, and literature which he might otherwise have missed.

By his third and last year at Cambridge, Charles could no longer elude his own assigned career and he had to work frantically to prepare for his final examinations in the classics, divinity, mathematics, and the rest. It was gruelling labor. "I have not stuck an insect this term," he complained. "Really I have not spirits or time to do anything," he wrote to William Fox. But he did work and managed to pass his examinations and come out tenth on the list.

In the interval between the New Year's tests and summer, Charles stayed at Cambridge to complete his residence requirement. He had nothing in particular to do but Henslow took charge of his favorite pupil in his own delightful way. Among the books he gave Charles to read, two had an important influence. One was Sir John Herschel's *Study of Natural Philosophy,* an excellent guide for a budding naturalist. The other was Alexander von Humboldt's *Travels.* Humboldt's descriptions of tropical America went to Charles' head.

From the time he was a small boy, he had longed to see all the plants and animals on earth.

At any rate, Humboldt was heady wine. Charles copied out long passages and on walks with Henslow and other friends would pull the magic pages out of his pocket and read them aloud. For some reason, he was most mesmerized by the descriptions of Teneriffe in the Canary Islands and its famous Sugar-Loaf peak. They must go and see this wondrous volcano for themselves. Henslow and a few others seemed almost as eager as Charles to make a pilgrimage to the Canaries. Charles made inquiries from a London merchant about ship schedules for the islands and studied Spanish in preparation for his dream trip.

At this point Henslow managed at last to introduce Charles to the great geologist, Adam Sedgwick and the young man forgot his vow never to have anything to do with the science. Instead, he was soon writing a friend, "It strikes me that all our knowledge about the structure of our earth is very much like what an old hen would know of a hundred-acre field, in a corner of which she is scratching." It was true that geology was in its infancy. By now Charles was possessed with an ambition to fill in the blank spaces of his own information and perhaps to contribute his mite to the world's stock of knowledge.

Sedgwick was a national figure, outstanding at Cambridge as a fine teacher and magnificent leader in field trips. It was thus a tribute to Charles, and to Henslow's powers of persuasion, that the great man consented to take young Darwin as his sole companion on a geology trip through North Wales in August.

The two spent a wonderful three weeks tramping through the mountains, scanning old rocks in search of fossils, and somehow failing to notice the scratches on these same rocks which told a story of glacial action. But that was still an unknown story. However, Charles learned much on the expedition because Sedgwick was a shrewd teacher. He would often send his neophyte on a parallel course to his own, for a day of making notes and collections, to be reported on when they met at the next inn.

The "first," that September day when the partridge shooting began, was still the most important date in Charles' calendar and he was home late in August to prepare for the shooting at Maer. His sisters gave him a little pile of mail waiting for him, and without any premonition he opened a letter from Cambridge. It was like standing on the peak of Teneriffe and seeing the whole world spread out at his feet.

Since the days of Captain James Cook, the British Admiralty had followed a tradition of scientific expeditions to the less known parts of the globe. Now the little brig *Beagle* was about to sail carrying a crew for the surveying of the South American coast, especially its southernmost tip; certain islands in the Pacific; and observations on the trip home around Africa. Its Captain, Robert Fitzroy, wanted a naturalist to study the land while he himself charted the coastal waters. No salary was offered and the naturalist must provide his own equipment and be willing to put up with the discomfort of cramped quarters. Fitzroy was grandson of a duke and nephew of Lord Castlereagh; naturally he must have a "gentleman" to share the cabin.

It happened that Henslow, and then Fitzroy's brother-in-law, also a scientist, were first invited, but neither of them felt able to leave home for a long voyage. Henslow then used his influence to have the invitation shifted to "Mr. Charles Darwin, grandson of Dr. Darwin the poet, as a young man of promising ability, extremely fond of geology, and indeed all branches of natural history," as Fitzroy described him to the Admiralty.

What Charles received that August evening was a letter

from Henslow and another from his old mathematics tutor Peacock, telling him that they had both recommended him and he could consider himself just about sure to be given the post. The *Beagle* would sail in a few weeks and Charles would have to make the right impression on Captain Fitzroy. The Admiralty had just told them they were to decide on the naturalist, which made the matter all but settled.

In a complete daze, Charles read the letters aloud to his sisters and could hardly believe his ears at their horrified comments. He could see the snowy peak of Teneriffe, the Andes, the South Pacific isles, the wonders of a voyage around the world. They could see nothing but dangerous storms, savages, bad smells, cockroaches, and all the menace of parts of the globe about which they knew nothing and cared less. When Dr. Darwin came home, it was the whole family against Charles, and though his father did take the precaution of postponing his final decision till morning, it was an unhappy evening.

Dr. Darwin must have been puzzled by those letters from Cambridge. Here was the Reverend Henslow writing his favorite pupil, "I have stated that I consider you to be the best qualified person that I know of . . . don't put on any modest doubts or fears about your disqualifications, for I assure you I think you are the very man they are in search of." And George Peacock, who had barely managed to pull Charles through mathematics, not only seemed to admire the "dunce," but was using some unsuspected influence with the Admiralty to get him this appointment.

Had he failed to appreciate his own son? At this crisis, the doctor could not bring himself to acknowledge any such thing. On the contrary, he felt these Cambridge zanies had led his son from the path toward the ministry into what he considered dangerous quicksands. So, in the next morning's interview, Dr. Darwin had only to ignore any possible value in Charles' excursions in the world of nature and to bring up his all-too-familiar record. After Charles had once more acknowledged his sins of running up Cambridge debts for frivolities, of sliding out of work, and all the rest, the young man was so sick with his own exaggerated sense of guilt that it was a simple matter to make him believe, for the moment, that the *Beagle* voyage was something no man in his senses should undertake.

Charles could not fight his father. He wrote his Cambridge champions that he could not sail on the *Beagle* and then he cleaned his guns and rode off to Maer.

Suddenly the world was transformed. His cousins were enraptured at this opportunity he had thrown up so hastily. Surely it wasn't too late! His mind began swinging like a pendulum. Was the voyage, after all, lost to him? His father had given him one loophole so small he considered it safe. "If you can find any man of common sense who advises you to go I will consent," he had said rather smugly.

Charles hadn't far to look for the man whose common sense was a byword with his father. In the evening, Uncle Jos went over the whole list of the doctor's objections and in a masterly letter to his brother-in-law answered every one. No, he did not think the trip would be "disreputable to Charles' character as a clergyman;" in fact, the study of natural history was entirely suitable for ministers and Charles was offered a rare chance of "seeing men and things." No, he did not think the voyage would unsettle Charles, even sailors were known to subside into "domestic and quiet habits" when they left the sea. No, it was hardly conceivable that the Admiralty would send out an unseaworthy vessel—and so on, down the list.

Along with this masterpiece went a touching letter from Charles to his father, begging him to reconsider. If the answer was no, "I should be most ungrateful if I did not implicitly yield to your better judgement and to the kindest indulgence which you have shown me all through my life."

But if his father answered yes, Charles would hurry directly to consult with Henslow.

Early the next morning Charles was off for the shooting but at ten Uncle Jos sent for him and hastened him into a waiting coach. He had decided that letters weren't enough, they had better see Dr. Darwin. His instinct was sound, the doctor gave in.

Charles, still guilty about his Cambridge debts, assured his father, "I would be deucedly clever to spend more than my allowance on board the *Beagle!*"

The huge man looked at his son, who had incredibly come out the victor in their first real battle.

"But they tell me that you *are* very clever," he squeaked in the tiny voice that was, for once, appropriate.

5

Anchors Aweigh

CHARLES WAS UP before three the next morning, speeding to Cambridge on the heels of his jubilant letter to Henslow with the news of Dr. Darwin's about face. He was dreadfully afraid that the *Beagle* post had already been given to somebody else. Henslow could reassure him on that but a new hitch had arisen. Captain Fitzroy had developed qualms about taking a naturalist, especially a perfect stranger, on a voyage that would last years. What was worse, he didn't seem to like what he had been told about Charles, perhaps the fact that he was a Whig. Fitzroy was, of course, a dyed-in-the-wool Tory.

Any rebuff was a mortal wound to Charles and he instantly abandoned all hopes of making the voyage. But Henslow understood him so perfectly and had such skill in reassuring his young friend, that Charles was soon on his way to London to see Fitzroy in person. He suffered agonies all the way and their morning interview began in an atmosphere of misgivings on both sides. Fitzroy was prepared not to like this obscure young Whig and Darwin was prepared not to be liked.

What saved him was his remarkable gift for sincere admiration of others. He forgot his own diffidence and low appraisal of himself in a sudden warm appreciation of Captain Fitzroy, who, as he wrote Susan after the interview, was everything delightful. "It is no use attempting to praise him as much as I feel inclined to do, for you would not believe me. One thing I am certain, nothing could be more open and kind than he was to me."

The ice melted rapidly. Fitzroy began to respond to Charles' charm, his beautiful manners, his enthusiasm for the voyage. One of his many queer habits was face reading. Like palmistry, the features revealed character and he felt that young Darwin's nose showed a lack of energy and determination. However, the nose and Darwin in general improved as the interview melted into an animated talk between two young men bent on exploring each other's minds.

Robert Fitzroy was only four years older than Charles, a dark, slender aristocrat (*his* nose suggested the eagle). He had entered the Navy at fourteen from the Royal Naval College, and in 1826, when he had come of age, he was a lieutenant on the *Beagle* during her previous voyage. This brig and her consort, the *Adventure*, were making a coastal survey of South America from Rio de Janeiro around Cape Horn and up to Chile. Britain, now humming with factories using the Boulton-Watt steam engines which had so fascinated Charles' grandfather, was opening up markets in South America. The Navy's part in this expansion was to get very precise charts of the harbors and waters of the South American continent for the use of British merchantmen—and in case of emergency—of battleships.

After two years of this survey, the *Beagle's* captain committed suicide in a fit of despondency and Fitzroy was put in command. He proved to be an excellent captain and his charts were perfection. Moreover, he was intelligent enough to realize the need for a study of the land as well as the sea and when the *Beagle* came home for a complete overhaul, he got permission from the Admiralty to take along a geologist-naturalist for the finish of the expedition.

At some point in their talk, Fitzroy decided that Darwin was the right man for the post and after that he was as kind as possible. He told Charles that he would make him as comfortable as he could and would put any books and instruments of his own at Charles' disposal. If it developed that the hardships of the voyage were too much, he guaranteed to release Charles and send him home from the first likely port. And then, for his own protection, he made a suggestion. He was sure they would get along well, and sure Charles wouldn't mind "being told that I want the cabin to myself when I want to be alone.—If we treat each other this way, I hope we shall suit; if not, probably we should wish each other at the devil."

Fitzroy made formal application to the Lords of Admiralty for Charles' appointment, which came through promptly. Charles was in a fever of preparation and Susan received almost daily lists of things to send him in London: a dozen new shirts, his carpet bag, slippers and shoes, his Spanish books, his compass and microscope. Besides the firearms he already had, he bought a fine rifle and a case of pistols. His arsenal was necessary for getting fresh meat, for protection against savages or brigands, and most of all for shooting every variety of bird and animal in South America.

He took a day off to see the coronation of King William IV, rather a dull affair except for the magnificent Horse Guards and the fireworks in the evening.

Soon he sailed around to Plymouth with Fitzroy for a look at the *Beagle*, dismasted and careened in the dockyard like a stranded whale. She was not impressive, a bare hundred

feet long and thirty wide and, at the moment, seemed an unlikely craft for a voyage around the world. He had to take
Fitzroy's word for it that the brig would soon be in fine
order and would prove big enough to carry her company of
more than seventy men.

Still not knowing of the delays in overhaul and the va-
garies of weather which would postpone the brig's sailing,
Charles was in a tremendous hurry, rejoicing that his return
to London by coach took only twenty-four hours. He went
up to Cambridge for a final briefing from Henslow, who
would take charge of the fossils, bird and animal skins,
plants and insects which Charles would send every now and
then, when he found a trustworthy captain bound for home.
He settled up his Cambridge debts, with a mixture of relief
and remorse at the expense of his old frivolities and his new
scientific equipment meant to his father—who was, after
all, a rich man.

Saying good-bye to Henslow, the dearest and best friend
of his youth, was hard for them both. It was quite in line
with his Merlin-like role of always influencing Charles in the
right direction that his last bit of advice was for Charles to
get a copy of Lyell's *Principles of Geology.* "You must read
it," he said, "but you must on no account accept Lyell's theories." This, the first volume of a work which was to explode
accepted ideas of geology, had already caused uneasiness
in the scientific world.

Charles had a last ten days at home and at Maer, such days
as he was to remember in intervals of homesickness which
were a positive agony. What wonderful people they were!
His family at the Mount came first in his devotion and leaving them now was painful.

Charles arrived in London early in October, only to find
that the *Beagle's* sailing had been postponed to November

4. He wrote his family, "What a glorious day the 4th of November will be to me! My second life will then commence, and it shall be as a birthday for the rest of my life."

He was not to celebrate that particular date as the birthday of C. Darwin, scientist. After a fortnight in London, where he improved his time by meeting various "great guns in the scientific world" he went by coach to Devonport near Plymouth, from which the brig would sail. Just when was now uncertain; the *Beagle* was far from ready and the season of southwest gales had set in. Charles made himself comfortable at an inn, where he read a good deal and wrote frequent letters home, conscious that each one was an anti-climax. He explored the pleasant Devon coast and countryside and with Lord Barrington rode to Exmoor to geologize. Now and then he would have breakfast or dinner with Fitzroy and the other officers, who were busily working to make the *Beagle* shipshape but who seemed to Charles to be completely callous about the weather. What seemed a calamity to him was familiar routine to these salt-water men. November brought its dismal rains and howling gales and short of abolishing November altogether there was nothing to be done.

On the 21st of that lamentable month, Charles moved his belongings to the brig. He was to share the poop cabin with Lieutenant J. L. Stokes, who amiably showed him how to arrange his belongings so that there was a place for everything—which had seemed out of the question at first. There were his clothes for a variety of climates, his reference books and guns, and his scientific equipment. Simple as this was, it took up room; telescope, microscope, compasses, magnets and magnifying glasses, notebooks and drawing materials, jointed nets for catching insects and bottles, pillboxes, alcohol for preserving specimens.

After he discovered what the sailor's knack for compact stowing could do in the poop cabin, he felt better about the small size of the *Beagle*. She was only two hundred and forty-two tons, broad in the beam, and notoriously given to rolling. But she had been completely rebuilt, with her deck raised and her tonnage increased to make her steadier, it was hoped, in heavy weather. The new copper plates set into her masts made her lightning-proof, removing one great worry from the Captain's mind.

By the end of the month, Charles, who had nothing to worry about but time, had worried himself into such a state that he imagined the palpitations and heart pains he was now having might mean something was really wrong with his heart. He dared not consult a doctor, who might forbid the trip.

On December 2, he had a joyful surprise. Erasmus, on his way home from the Continent, stopped to see his brother off. He saw him off on the 4th, and again on the 10th. This time the *Beagle* actually got out to sea, and Erasmus, who was no doubt tired of a succession of farewell dinners, departed for Shrewsbury. The next day the *Beagle* was back in port and Charles, who had suffered agonies of seasickness as the brig wallowed in a heavy gale, made all haste back to the inn and a steady bed.

For several days he doubted if he could survive another day of seasickness, let alone several years of it. But he was bravely aboard when the brig sailed out again on December 21, only to encounter another storm which drove her aground on a rock off Drake's Island. Back in port, she was found to have suffered no harm to her keel and Charles, who had spent a fairly comfortable night in his hammock, began to hope that these rehearsals would help him get his sea legs.

Two days after Christmas, the *Beagle* finally got a fair wind and was well at sea before the new year of 1832. Charles was too wretched to care; he lay in his hammock, green in the face, racked with all the agonies of seasickness.

He was sorry that he had ever set foot in this torture chamber of a ship, which wallowed and rolled hour after hour in the heavy swells of the Bay of Biscay. The worst of sea travel was the fact that there was no let up, no reprieve. Unless you ended your misery by jumping overboard, you had to stay with the ship, enduring today's misery with little hope that tomorrow would be better.

Captain Fitzroy was most sympathetic. Now and then Charles would stagger into his cabin and the Captain would assure him that the *Beagle* behaved better in the calm waters of the South Atlantic. He talked along in a comforting and always interesting way, hoping to lift poor Darwin out of the doldrums. Charles was grateful for these friendly ministrations, but he was growing weak because all he could hold down was raisins—not the best diet for a young man of his big build.

By January 5, he was well enough to make the first entry in his diary, which merely recorded his inauspicious start as world traveler. But the Captain was right; as the brig sailed into calmer waters she steadied, and so did Charles' stomach. By the next day, he was able to bask in the sun and enjoy the incredible blue of the sea. They were nearing Africa and the Canaries which lie about sixty miles off its coast.

At dawn on January 6, Darwin had his first sight of Teneriffe and its mountain, of which he had dreamed the whole last year. The Sugar Loaf, with its snowy crest, rose above the clouds, twice as high as he had imagined it. It towered two and a half miles above the sea, its base banked in mist. He had never seen anything as exquisite. Soon he would land and, like Humboldt, climb the volcano's flanks, toiling up and up to the pure, snow-filled crater.

Just as they were preparing to anchor, a boat came alongside bearing the British vice-consul. There had been rumors of a cholera epidemic in England, he told the Captain, and ships from British ports had been put under a twelve days' quarantine.

To Charles this was like a "death warrant. . . . Those who have never experienced it can scarcely conceive what a gloom it cast on every one," he wrote in his diary. The deepest gloom was in his own heart, for the seasoned men around him were used to disappointments. The Captain reacted instantly; they had sailed three months later than the original schedule and they could not afford twelve days idling off Teneriffe. He ordered all sails set; they would push along to the next station, the Cape Verde Islands.

But the wind died and for another day they lay becalmed. For another day Charles could feast his eyes on the peak of Teneriffe, so perfect in its visible beauty, so important to him as a symbol of some final mystery toward which he would travel all his life. Now it was to remain a symbol, perhaps better left inviolate.

6

University at Sea

It was a happy run to the Cape Verde Islands, for the weather was balmy and the sea quiet enough to reassure Charles about his ability to finish the voyage. He had only to pray for good weather, when he felt as well as anybody on the ship. In spells of bad weather, he would have to take to his hammock, but usually he could get some reading done. This proved to be his pattern during the voyage which stretched out to five years, but which was to include long intervals when he worked ashore, with the *Beagle* off on her own concerns.

No matter how he felt, his reading had now become of great importance. He had been recommended for this expedition as a naturalist, but he was untrained and almost unread in science. He must live up to his assignment; more important, the first prickings of ambition had begun, the personal ambition to amount to something in his own eyes. That meant taking up a big slack, for he had never really worked at any branch of science and had not even learned how to work.

This was not altogether his own fault. He grew up in a sort of dead center between two eras. The old way of looking at the world of nature he had seen doddering into senility at Edinburgh. There his professors had regarded every aspect of man and nature as a literal supplement to the first chapter of Genesis, which described how everything was created, once and for all. At Cambridge, the modern age was in sight, just over the horizon, but there were few men bold enough to see that Genesis was a great creation myth, a beautiful allegory expressing the mystery of life's beginnings, but never pretending to explain it.

Even Henslow, for all his knowledge of nature, belonged to the old school of scientific-religious thought which was due for a terrific explosion. He had, as a broad-minded man, urged Charles to read the first volume of Charles Lyell's book on geology, which had just come out. It proved to be a charge of dynamite which cleared the way, in Darwin's mind at least, for the coming era of true science.

It was actually Charles' luck that he had read less and thus accumulated less debris to be cleared away. For Lyell's book, which he was far from understanding or agreeing with for some time, gave him a method. He read it at the best possible time, sailing down into a new world which he could study with his own eyes. Lyell showed him the scientific method—working from the known to the unknown, observing a multitude of facts as carefully and objectively as he possibly could, and then, perhaps, building up a theory to explain these facts and bring them all together in a great orderly scheme.

Charles had already observed enough fossils and living creatures to make him feel that the world was far older than most people believed. It was no longer the fashion to accept the exact date of the creation of the planet as calculated by

Archbishop Ussher, at nine o'clock on the morning of October 12, 4004 B.C. And yet Charles had to walk only a few steps to the Captain's cabin to find an extremely intelligent man who was just as literal-minded about Creation. Fitzroy believed the world was created in seven *days*, as Genesis seemed to say, though liberals took the word to mean *ages*. Fitzroy argued, "Vegetation was produced on the third day, the sun on the fourth. If the third day was an age, how was the vegetable world nourished?" This logic was actually to be printed in his report of the voyage later on but his ideas were firmly set at the period when Charles was receiving his first charge of dynamite from Charles Lyell.

It was something like the shock he had received walking along the tidal pools near Edinburgh, when his friend Grant had linked the ideas of Lamarck with those of Charles' grandfather. Then, for the first time, he had inklings of a new theory—the continual, gradual creation of the world by natural processes. Erasmus Darwin had set Lamarck thinking, Lamarck had inspired Lyell in his youth, and now Lyell was giving Charles Darwin an electric shock.

Without ever dismissing the poetic story in Genesis, or dropping his own religious faith, Lyell had drawn a line separating the mystery of man's arrival on the planet from his own subject, geology. The rocks told him they were ancient indeed, that the earth's crust had been changing for a very long time and was continuing to change under one's eyes. This was not new; by 1785, the Scot, James Hutton was describing the continuous cycle of building-up and erosion which was forever transforming the earth. "In the phenomena of the earth, I see no vestige of a beginning, no prospect of an end," he announced boldly. Then William Smith, "father of English geology," discovered that fossil groups followed one another in stratas of rock, the most primitive animals in the lowest layers, very slowly changing their forms as the rocks were very slowly built up.

Charles himself had been interested in Smith's colored geologic maps and had attempted to make one of his familiar Shropshire region the summer before. His own map had told a story of very gradual change. Now Lyell gave him the next bold step; to produce what we actually see written in the rocks would require not thousands but millions of years. Never mind about how or when God created man. The earth, with its myriads of plants and animals, had been in existence for millions of years and had been changing by natural processes.

Given time without limit, earth explained itself. Slowly continents were thrust up by volcanic forces under the sea, slowly these continents were whittled down by moving glaciers, rain and snow, frost and sandstorms. Slowly rivers cut their deep valleys and built up their great plains and deltas.

This immense, majestic story is familiar now. To Charles, it must have been like standing on Teneriffe's peak to discover a larger world.

At St. Jago, their port in the Cape Verde group, Charles was given a vivid application of Lyell's theory. It began with the impressions of his first tropical landing: the streets teeming with naked children of every shade from black to gold, with pigs and goats and dogs. He feasted on oranges bought at a hundred for a shilling and tasted his first banana, which he found "mawkish sweet and flavorless." He was overwhelmed with the luxuriance of life and color; the tamarinds and palms, the brilliant flowers, and implausibly brilliant birds. All this life flourishing on a long dead and harmless volcano!

During the three weeks' stay at St. Jago, Charles explored the flora and fauna with great enthusiasm, but his mind was on geology. When they had entered the harbor of Porto Praia in the Cape Verde Islands, he had been struck by a horizontal band of white running for miles along the sea cliff, about forty-five feet above the water. He took the first opportunity to investigate this straight white ribbon and found it was a layer of lime in which myriads of sea-shells had been embedded. They were like the shells lying on the beach below the cliff. The cliff itself rested on ancient volcanic rock. Above the white band there was a layer of basalt, solidified lava.

Applying Lyell's theory, Darwin could reconstruct how this curious cliff had come into being. A stream of molten lava had flowed over the bottom of the sea, with its white shells. The hot lava had turned a section of the sea's bed into crystalline limestone, with the shells baked fast into the stone. Then, later on, the whole island was heaved up by more volcanic action from under the sea and the sea's bottom was pushed high above the water to appear now as an even white band. How clear Lyell made it all seem!

Every day he went ashore on field trips. The island had luxuriant growth where there was water, but since it had not rained for an entire year, great areas with no streams or rivers were merely dry lava plains, supporting few creatures but kingfishers which fed on grasshoppers and lizards. In collecting marine specimens, Charles was fascinated by the cuttlefish and received his baptism as a naturalist from one wily old fellow who played a long game of changing his color so that Charles could not see him in the water, and then, safely hidden under a rock, he ejected a stream of water which hit Charles squarely in the face.

Though specimens were few on the island, Charles was already getting the sense of independent work and even a vision of making that work count for something in the world of science. Resting one noon below a lava cliff, he thought about all the geological wonders he would see in the voyage around the world. Surely this would make a valuable book! It had never occurred to him that he was capable of writing a book of real importance. Now his mind raced ahead and he could already see that his account of the voyage must include not only geology, but descriptions of plants and animals. This vision was quite unlike his childish daydreams of doing something so remarkable that everybody would realize young Charles was Somebody. This was a rapidly maturing Charles getting a sense of his own hidden powers. He recognized then, and remembered always, this noonday hour on St. Jago as a turning point in his career.

As the *Beagle* made for the coast of Brazil, Darwin the scientist settled into the routine he was to follow for the rest of his life. It could be expressed in three words: constant careful work. With Lyell's method as a guide, he now knew how to work. Close and accurate observation was the first requirement, but here he had only to develop his inherited gift for seeing details or connections most people missed; indeed, he had been a remarkable observer all his life. The next thing was records; each invaluable, vivid impression must be set down at once. "Trust nothing to memory" was one of his strict rules. These rough but precise field notes were then expanded in his diary as promptly as possible, when the details and the over-all picture were still fresh in his mind.

His on-the-scene notes were sketches which omitted all but the essential lines: "Small black ant putting everything to flight; spiders and blatta in great agitation—a brick stopped their course. . . ." "Saw a cormorant catch a fish & let it go 8 times . . . like a cat does a mouse or an otter a fish."

He was sending Henslow sections of his journal and consignments of specimens from time to time and he kept careful records of when and by whom these precious notes and specimens were taken to England. Everything was carefully wrapped, tagged, and numbered. Later there would be times when his casks and crates crowded the decks, waiting for a homebound vessel and Lieutenant Wickham would growl, "If I were skipper, I'd soon have you and all your damned mess out of the place."

Such growls came from affection. The whole ship's company treated Charles like a favorite, if eccentric, brother. They called him "Flycatcher" and "dear old Philosopher;" they were fascinated by his mysterious goings-on, and often one or two of the junior officers would join his field trips and cheerfully help him lug the day's finds back to the brig. Captain Fitzroy himself would sometimes volunteer as naturalist's apprentice.

The Captain was delighted with Charles and wrote his superior at the Admiralty: "Darwin is a very sensible hard-working man, and a very pleasant mess-mate. I never saw a 'shore-going fellow' come in the ways of a ship so soon and so thoroughly as Darwin. . . . D. is equally liked and respected by every person in this ship."

For a Navy Captain, something of a martinet even in those days when floggings and rigid discipline were the rule, to praise Charles for his quick adaptation to life at sea—this was a tribute. Charles detested the sea, as only a man cursed with incurable seasickness can do. He liked the order and ant hill industry of the *Beagle* as a good background for his own sort of order and hard work but the *Beagle* meant cramped quarters for body and spirit. There were many reasons why Darwin should have found it all but impossible to adapt to life on a Navy ship. He not only succeeded in adjusting but he was to pile up an unbroken record of keeping the peace with all his shipmates.

This means that there was more in Charles Darwin than the unusually sweet temper and tact of his Darwin-Wedgwood family. By the time he sailed off, he had developed a remarkable self-control. It was tested day after day in his contacts with Fitzroy, who was an explosive mixture of qualities. Charles warmly admired his devotion to his ship and his work, his bursts of charming generosity, his brilliance, though it was a narrow-minded brilliance. But he never knew what to expect of Fitzroy, who was apt to be seized with fits of almost insane rage, often with no provocation except his own tense nerves. Everybody on the brig was on the lookout for these seizures, which were worst in the morning. When the eight o'clock watch came on deck, there was a code inquiry about the breakfast coffee. If it was reported "hot" that meant that the skipper was having one of his attacks and was to be avoided if possible.

Charles, as the only man on board who was not under Fitzroy's direct orders, was treated as a colleague and companion. At one, they dined alone together in the Captain's cabin and their overlapping scientific interests often threw them together for long evening discussions. As well-bred young men with lively minds, they were both bent on making themselves agreeable and their relation was pleasant enough, as long as they avoided dangerous topics.

Always on his guard with the Captain, Charles was wholly at ease with the others; talkative Sulivan and the growling, admirable Wickham; his cabin-mate John Stokes who was assistant surveyor. He spent many hours in the chart room watching Stokes turn out the wonderful mariner's charts which the Admiralty would soon publish with justified pride. The poop cabin boy, Covington, became Flycatcher's apprentice, learning to shoot and skin the birds for Darwin's collection. And then there was Midshipman Arthur Mellersh, who introduced himself by announcing, "I am Mellersh of Midhurst. I have read Lord Byron and I don't care a damn for anyone."

The most exotic people on board were three natives of Tierra del Fuego. On the previous voyage, Fitzroy had taken four Fuegians on board the *Beagle*, three of them as hostages for a stolen whaleboat. The fourth was Jemmy Button, so called because he was bought from his parents in exchange for one pearl button. On a whim, Fitzroy decided to take these primitive folk back to England for a short course in the Christian religion and for display as curiosities. (The tradition of bringing home such exhibits had started with Captain Cook). One of the men died of smallpox soon after he reached England, which left a man, girl and Jemmy Button to be tutored and presented in the routine way to the king and queen. Now Fitzroy was dutifully returning his protegés to their native land, shepherded by a missionary called Matthews, whom nobody on board particularly liked.

Tierra del Fuego was still far away and far in the future. But South America was actually visible on the last day of February—a brilliant green line on the horizon. By noon, the *Beagle* dropped anchor off Bahia, (Salvador) a town in northern Brazil.

7

Brazilian Forest to Argentine Pampas

BRAZIL'S OLDEST CITY, with its lofty houses and long elegant windows, is nestled in a luxuriant wood on a steep bank overlooking the great bay of All Saints. The convents, porticos, and public buildings and the fine view of the bay struck Charles, but "these beauties were as nothing compared to the Vegetation." He remembered his first sight of a tropical forest as the greatest experience of his life.

Wandering by himself the next day in the Brazilian forest he was at a loss as to what was most striking; the richness of the vegetation, the glossy green of the foliage, or the strangeness of the parasitical plants. Entwining their tendrils around lofty trees, some still flourishing, others dead or rotten trunks, these delicate-looking plants were sapping the energy of the giant hosts on which they lived. All around him he saw this evidence of the unceasing struggle of the living to survive.

No sooner was he bewildered by some strange fruit or tree than his eye was drawn to a brightly colored butterfly!

As he watched the exotic insect on its visit to a flower, he was dazzled by the greater brilliance of the flower on which it alighted. In this splendor, "the mind is a chaos of delight." It was like something out of the Arabian Nights.

Perhaps it was the strange mixture of sound and silence of these woods that touched him most; the noise of insects, so loud that in the evening it could be heard on the vessel anchored several hundred yards from shore, while "within the recesses of the forest a universal silence" reigned. Or was it perhaps the darkness, penetrated only by spots of sunlight through the entangled mass of parasitic plants which formed a thick ceiling over the forest?

A curious fungus he encountered set him thinking. As he examined it in his hand, a beetle settled on it. Like the *Hymenophallus* he knew in England, this fungus attracted beetles by its disagreeable odor. Strange that in Brazil and in England, an ocean apart, these two different species of plant and insect had a similar attraction for each other. Here was an intriguing observation that demanded an explanation! If the English and Brazilian fungus had each been separately created, how did both develop the same habit of life, the same relationship between beetle and fungus?

Before returning to the landing place, he was caught in a tropical storm. Under the shelter of a tree, so thick that it would never have been penetrated by ordinary English rain, he saw a torrent flowing down the trunk. To this violence of the downpour, he attributed the richness of the green carpet on the forest floor. Tropical luxuriance was everywhere—in the cultivated areas of coconut, banana, plantain, oranges, papaws mingled with patches of Indian corn, yams, and cassava, as well as in the wild growth of the forest.

As often happened when the *Beagle's* men were busy taking soundings, Charles was permitted to remain ashore. On one such occasion while wandering in the country around Bahia with a young boy as interpreter, he had walked for hours in the heat of the sun and stopped at a wayside inn for refreshment. He was soon surrounded by a crowd of men, women, and children who were astonished by the strange equipment that came out of his enormous pockets. "Full, full of sin" was their comment about compass, pistol, and fly net —for who but "el Diabolo" would possess such curious things? But after he shared his wine with them, he was sent on his way with courteous and dignified bows. In the evening he stopped at a hotel, where with three carefully chosen words—*comer, cama,* and *pagar*—he obtained *food* and a *bed* for which he offered to *pay.*

On another day, Rowlett and he wandered through the narrow streets near the wharves with all their litter and water front smells. Around the warehouses they saw the heavy labor done by black men, bent under staggering burdens, and beating time to the rhythm of their own song.

Days of geologizing and botanizing followed. On a trip with King, he collected numberless beetles and a most beautiful lizard, while King shot some birds. Then, to his great annoyance, a sore, swollen knee kept him idle for several days.

Fitzroy was busy making his first reports and with what energy he worked! "If he does not kill himself, he will during this voyage do a wonderful quantity of work," wrote Darwin.

However, Fitzroy did not neglect the traditional courtesies between Navy Captains. On the 12th of March, he gave a grand dinner on the quarterdeck for the amusing Captain Paget of H.M.S. *Samerang,* who often paid them visits. The talk turned to the subject of slavery, which precipitated a violent quarrel between Fitzroy and Darwin and almost ended the voyage for Charles. On this subject the Captain and the naturalist were at opposite poles. Paget described the brutal treatment of slaves in Brazil and said that even the best-treated ones wished to return to their native land. In his wanderings, Darwin had himself seen many instances of cruelty and had heard of the kidnapping of children for sale in the open market, the separation of families, and other forms of inhumanity. He fully shared his family's hatred of slavery.

Fitzroy, brought up as a Tory, defended the property rights of the slave owner. Returning to the subject after Paget had gone he argued, "I have myself heard slaves say, when asked by their master, that they were satisfied with their lot."

"And what do you think such testimony given by a slave in the presence of his master is worth?" Darwin countered.

This was too much for the furious Captain. Did Mr. Darwin doubt him, he raged? If so, there was no room for both of them on the *Beagle!*

Charles was fully prepared to leave but when word of the Captain's fury got round, the gun room officers asked Darwin to mess with them. After a few hours, when Fitzroy's anger was spent, an apology followed with a request that Charles should stay on.

From then on, Darwin went out of his way to avoid quarrels with the Captain and everybody on shipboard. Sulivan once declared that during the whole voyage he had never known Darwin to be out of temper or say a hasty or unkind word to anyone.

Darwin and Fitzroy profoundly disagreed on how plants and animals came into existence. While their work led them to see the same things, their interpretations were worlds apart. This difference between them became ever sharper as Darwin's inquiring mind found accumulating evidence of the vastness of the geological timetable. As Charles moved farther and farther away from the creed of Special Creation, Fitzroy must often have doubted his own wisdom in choosing Darwin as naturalist.

When the charting of the harbor was over, they were again on their way, sailing south. Farewell to delightful Bahia with its beautiful skies and landscape!

But the sea had its own excitements. One day Charles saw a waterspout a few miles away. First the sky was darkened by a black bank of clouds from which hung a pointed projection like a cow's tail. Then a spiralling funnel-shaped column of mist and spray produced by a whirlwind seemed to grow out of the sea, rising to meet the cloud. A few moments later the cloud mass disappeared, to be followed by a heavy rainstorm. Had the mass approached too close to the *Beagle* a big gun would have been fired to break it up. Otherwise there would have been danger of the waterspout's swamping the vessel.

There was more excitement when a large shark following the ship was harpooned and caught on a baited hook. But the hook broke and the shark escaped. Two days later, Darwin created a sensation by catching a young shark with a hook baited with a piece of salt pork.

There were quiet days spent in study and arranging of collections and inexpressibly beautiful nights under the phosphorescent Clouds of Magellan and the Southern Cross.

Late in March, they cruised among the Abrolhos Islands, sounding and taking angles, and then under a fine breeze headed for Rio de Janeiro. Soon after midnight on April 1, there was a great commotion on board. One by one the men were called up on deck in their shirts; carpenters to repair a leak, quartermasters to see to a sprung mast, midshipmen to reef topsails. Then Sulivan called for Charles: "Darwin, did you ever see a grampus? Bear a hand, then." Jumping out of his hammock, Charles rushed on deck, all eagerness, to be received by a roar of laughter from the whole watch. April fool!

On the 3rd, they had a full view of the harbor of Rio with

its hubbub of shipping and porpoises, sharks and turtles, darting and weaving in and around the ship. Tomorrow would be a great day for awaiting them were letters and newspapers from home, the first since they had left Plymouth over three months before.

On April 5th, Charles was replying to Caroline's letter of December 3rd and describing the "gaudy" city of Rio, with its towers and cathedrals and its vast bay, dotted with ships flying the flags of every nation.

They had dropped anchor the night before but didn't dock until morning, for the Captain was determined to give his men their first view of the magnificent harbor in broad daylight. The flagship of the British South American station was at Rio and they came in "first rate style" alongside the Admiral's ship. Then, Charles wrote, the *Beagle's* crew "took in every inch of canvas, and then immediately set it again . . . It is a great satisfaction to know that we are in such beautiful order and discipline," he added proudly.

In the middle of these naval flourishes, the bundle of letters arrived. "Send them below," thundered Wickham, "every fool is looking at them and neglecting his duty." In about an hour, Charles succeeded in getting his mail and he rushed below, "there to feast over the thrilling enjoyment" of reading all the family news.

Continuing the letter to Caroline the next day, he told of his plans to accompany a merchant to a large estate a hundred and fifty miles away and then to spend two weeks in a virgin forest, inhabited by wild beasts: "You will all be terrified at the thought of my combating with Alligators and Jaguars in the wilds of Brazil." While he reassured his loved ones about the safety of the expedition, he was in fact facing real dangers. The jaguars, living on small wooded islands, caught fish and hunted the capybara, similar to a guinea pig. But they were also known to kill human beings, often woodcutters who failed to recognize their tracks. They even boarded ships to hunt for victims.

The first night Charles and his guide rode through forest, desert, and marsh in the dim light of the moon, until at last they arrived at an inn where they were glad to dismount and lie down on the straw mats. Before sunrise, they left their miserable sleeping place, riding along a road lying between the sea and salt lagoons. Here were egrets and cranes, beautiful fishing birds, succulent plants of fantastic forms, among the deliciously fragrant orchids.

The next inn was a very good one, by the standards of those parts. The large house had no floor or glazed windows but was well roofed, while the bedrooms provided wooden platforms covered with thin straw mats for the weary traveler's bed. As for dinner, the innkeeper assured them he could provide them with anything they wanted.

"Any soup?"

"No, sir."

"Bread?"

"Not tonight."

"Dried meat?"

"Oh no, sir."

After two hours, they were given a meal of fowl, rice, and farina. Often guests had to kill their own meat for dinner. Darwin was shocked by the filth, lack of eating utensils, and the cheating and disagreeable manners he found at these inns.

But there were other times when he was the guest of wealthy Brazilian ranch owners on their vast *estancias*, on which grazed thousands of cattle, goats, and sheep, and horses. Oranges and bananas grew in profusion close to the houses. The surrounding woods were full of game and a deer would be killed for the special guest.

On such occasions "if the tables do not groan, the guests

surely do," he complained. Because of his digestive troubles,
Darwin was often distressed because it was considered most
discourteous to refuse any dish. One day, when he thought
he had dutifully finished the meal, he was dismayed to see a
roast turkey and pig brought to the table. He had to start all
over again.

The arrival of a stranger was announced by the ringing of
bells and the firing of cannons and the host always could be
depended on to offer horses, pack animals, guides, and
hunters to accompany the guest wherever he wanted to go.
These rich ranchers lived like nabobs but they were hardly
well-informed. They asked him amazing questions: Did he
really believe that the world was round? Had he ever in his
travels been in danger of falling off the edge of the earth
into space? Was it hotter or colder to the north? Is it the
earth or the sun that moves?

Back from his expedition, Charles took a cottage for a few
weeks in Botafogo near the city. On the day he moved his
belongings from the *Beagle* to Botafogo, he experienced
something of the horrors of a shipwreck. Heavy swells
swamped the whaleboat as they were landing on the beach
and before his eyes, his books, instruments, and gun cases
were floating away. Fortunately everything was recovered
without too much damage. For eleven weeks he remained
on shore, while the *Beagle* returned to Bahia to settle once
and for all its correct longitude.

Charles made many excursions into the forest, collecting
innumerable fresh-water creatures and insects. In cultivated
areas, he studied the tea tree, "an insignificant little bush,"
and the camphor, sago, cinnamon, clove, and breadfruit
trees.

He hunted small deer, pachas (which looked like guinea
pigs), and parrots but soon gave up shooting to concentrate

on geologizing, observing, and reflecting. He hired a native to shoot birds and animals for his collections.

All too soon the *Beagle* was back and in early July they sailed south to Uruguay and Argentina. Darwin planned to take trips into the pampas, the vast treeless plains of these countries.

Traveling south on the continent after crossing the Salado River, he was struck with the change from the coarse scrubby vegetation to a "carpet of fine green verdure." The grass suddenly became short, bright green with beds of clover and thistles. Was this due to a change in the nature of the soil? The inhabitants with whom he took every opportunity to talk about such local matters told him that the green cover was the result of grazing cattle which, of course, manured their pasturage. Did this mean the introduction of a new species, a change in the growth of the old, or a mixture of the two? The answer he noted in his diary was: "We thus have lines of richly manured land serving as channels of communication across wide districts." Under new conditions, plants change; in fact, new ones appear. But how?

Soon he found other evidence of change. The Spaniards had introduced the prickly artichoke or cardoon into South America. Bordering the Uruguay River, the whole countryside had become choked up with this plant, which the botanists said was the common artichoke run wild. This prickly plant had grown into giant thistles to a height and thickness that made their immense beds impenetrable by man and beast. An intelligent farmer told him that in a deserted garden, he had seen the planted artichokes degenerating into this plant. Wherever these beds spread no other plant could live. Darwin commented: "an invasion on so grand a scale of one plant over the aborigines" showed how in the struggle for living space a new plant had overcome the old.

There were still more examples. Since 1535, when the first Spanish colonists landed with their domestic animals, countless herds of horses, cattle, and sheep had not only altered the vegetation but had almost banished the native guanaco, deer, and ostrich. The pig displaced the peccary and, with the introduction of domestic animals, there appeared also a large number of carrion vultures.

At Punta Alta he made a momentous discovery—fossil deposits of animals long extinct. Out of the reddish mud and gravel, he dug up one day, the head of a large animal that he judged to be related to the rhinoceros. It took him three hours to get it out of the rock and many more hours to carry his prize on board. The next day he returned to the same place and obtained another find—a jaw bone with a tooth, which he identified as belonging to the great *Megatherium*. Again and again he dug, finding other giants of the past—one of the huge anteaters, an armored animal like an armadillo, and three kinds of gnawing animals. Within an area of two hundred yards, he excavated the fossil remains of nine huge animals—"a perfect catacomb for monsters of extinct races."

The prize among these was the *Toxodon*, a rodent the size of an elephant with teeth like a rat. This giant pachyderm, a four-legged, vegetarian beast, was the ancestor of the small aquatic animals like the dugong and manatee. Buried with the giants were sea shells like the ones he now came across on the beach. What puzzled him was that the living forms were so similar and yet so much smaller than the extinct creatures.

How did so many species become extinct? And why were the new forms smaller? Had the creative force weakened? If so, then why were the marine shells on the beach so much like the ones he found buried? He didn't yet have the answers, but as he discovered more facts, he was able to dismiss the accepted idea of a stupendous catastrophe wiping out so many of the same species in the Old and the New World; in North America and in Siberia, on the other side of Bering Strait.

He found a quite different explanation. Traveling through the country he learned of the periodic droughts in the region. The latest *gran seco* had lasted from 1827 to 1830. There was so little rain that all vegetation, even the thistles, had died.

Great numbers of birds, wild animals, and cattle perished for lack of food and water. Wild deer, he was told, came to drink from courtyard wells; the partridges had hardly the strength to fly when pursued. As the brooks dried up, millions of head of cattle perished. In search of water, thousands of them stampeded the brackish waters of the river mouths, those arriving first being overwhelmed and crushed by those that followed. Some died from drinking the salty water, others, too weak to climb the banks, drowned, and the remainder fell exhausted over the corpses and died of hunger. The dust over the wasteland blew away all landmarks of the *estancias*, so that the owners could not tell the limits of their estates.

Soon after the drought a season of heavy rain caused great floods. Thousands of the skeletons must have been buried by the deposits of the very next year. What would a future geologist excavating this enormous collection of bones imbedded in the thick earthy mass say? "Would he not attribute it to a flood having swept over the surface of the land, rather than to common order of things?" he musingly noted in his diary.

Did Darwin ask this question, tongue in cheek? Was "the common order of things" the slow, gradual geological change?

At the bottom of the cliff, he discovered beds containing shark's teeth and shells of extinct marine animals. In the layers above these—hardened calcareous rock mixed with red clay—he found the bones of the land animals. This vertical section clearly told the story of a large bay of salt water, gradually filled up by sinking land until it became a muddy estuary. Into this the floating carcasses had been swept, he reasoned.

In addition to the mastodon and toxodon skeletons, Darwin found a single horse tooth in the pampas deposit. It revealed the existence of a native South American horse which had become extinct. The countless living herds were the descendants of the few introduced with the Spanish colonists. (It was well-known that no horse was living in America at the time of its discovery by Columbus.)

Darwin knew that Lyell had discovered a similar horse tooth in the United States. This led him along a new train of thought. The two Americas had been divided not by the Isthmus of Panama, but by the great Mexican plateau which prevented the migration of species. This barrier, rising some 7000 feet, affected the climate and divided the two continents into two separate zoological provinces. With the exception of a few species which were able to pass the barrier, this break led to the development of different mammals in the continents: giant gnawers, monkeys, llama, peccary, tapir, opossums, sloths, anteaters, and armadillos in South America; the hollow-horned ruminants (the ox, sheep, goat, and antelope), the elephant, mastodon, and horse in North America.

The horse, like many other extinct mammals, had once lived on both continents. The changes came only after the rise of the Mexican barrier. Darwin thought it was also probable that the North American mastodons, elephants, and hollow-horned ruminants migrated from the Siberian area across a land bridge, since submerged, near Bering Strait. In the same way, he said, the mammals of the West Indies indicate that the islands were once a land mass united to South America and were later separated by the sinking of all but the highest parts of the land, which now remained above the ocean as islands.

Thus the naturalist, reasoning from Lyell's principles, explained the development of new plant and animal species by separation, a result of the continuous elevations and subsidences of the land.

Part of Darwin's great finds, along with his notes on them, were sent to Henslow. These aroused great excitement in England, especially the discovery of the horse's tooth. The proud teacher and friend passed them on to Sedgwick, who wrote to Charles' old headmaster, Dr. Butler, praising Darwin's admirable work and priceless collection. "It was the best thing in the world for him that he went out on this voyage of discovery," Sedgwick wrote. "There was some risk of his turning out an idle man but his character will now be fixed, and if God spares his life he will have a great name among the naturalists of Europe."

News of the letter from this highly respected scientist soon reached the Mount and Maer and eventually got to Charles, who was as astonished at the praise as anybody in the family.

8

Tierra del Fuego

"Hurrah for Cape Horn and the Land of Storms," Charles wrote Henslow in November. They had spent the last month in the cities of Buenos Aires and Montevideo, and he was impatient to leave civilization and begin the next stage of work in the wilder parts of the continent. For a year and a half the *Beagle* would swing back and forth around the southern tip of South America, where much surveying remained to be done. Since they would be far from cities, they stocked up quantities of supplies. Even the officers' cabins were crammed with sacks of flour and sugar. The Captain was determined that no lack of food should interrupt his ambitious schedule.

Charles' own provisions for the voyage were mostly books and letters from home, to be read and re-read during the coming stormy days which would keep him in his hammock. To his delight, a bundle of letters arrived before the brig sailed. "Dear old Erasmus" had been running errands for him but had not succeeded in sending all the books he had asked for, they were either too expensive or were not to be found in the bookstores. Writing to Caroline, Charles reminded her that any books of travel by naturalists were what interested him most.

> "I am become quite devoted to Nat. History," he went on. "You cannot imagine what a fine miserlike pleasure I enjoy when examining an animal differing widely from any known genus . . . I am glad the *Journal* arrived safe: as for showing it, I leave that entirely in your hands. I suspect the first part is abominably childish, if so do not sent it to Maer. Also do not send it by coach (it may appear *ridiculous* to you), but I would as soon lose a piece of my memory as it . . ."

In the middle of December—which was midsummer in this latitude—they arrived at Tierra del Fuego, Land of Fire. Whalers and other voyagers who had come this way years before had discovered that as a ship approached the coast, the first natives to sight the vessel would light a fire to signal to the others. These fires led the earliest travelers to give the region its name.

Everyone on board was eager to see the Fuegian savages. The rising smoke at various points told them that natives were living there. Through spyglasses, the *Beagle* passengers could see a group of Indians, evidently watching the vessel with interest.

The next afternoon they anchored in Good Success Bay under the gaze of a party of Fuegians perched on a peak overhanging the sea, who greeted the strangers with yells and wild waving of their cloaks made of guanaco skins, the fur of a llama-like animal.

During the night, severe winds, rain, and heavy squalls swept from the mountains toward the small vessel. "Those

who know the comfortable feeling of hearing the rain &
wind beating against the windows whilst seated round a
fire will understand our feeling." Still, Darwin was grateful
to be safe in this bay. Here, Captain Cook in 1771 had made
his first anchorage off the South American coast. Here, his
landing party had nearly perished during a blizzard shortly
after their vessel the *Endeavor* dropped anchor. The
Beagle, arriving in December during the antarctic summer,
avoided the perils faced by Joseph Banks and Dr. Solander,
the naturalists in Cook's company, when they attempted to
climb the steep mountainside and were overtaken by a
severe snow storm.

The next morning, Captain Fitzroy sent a party of officers
to communicate with the Fuegians. As soon as the boat
came within hail, one of the savages advanced with shouts
to meet them and pointed out a good landing place. The
women and children all disappeared, alarmed at the sight
of strangers. Watching the gesticulating, shouting, almost
naked natives, Darwin could scarcely believe that such a
wide gap existed between savage and civilized man. It was
greater than between wild and domesticated animals, since
man had greater powers of improvement.

The chief spokesman, probably the head of the family,
wore a white feather cap over his long black hair. There
was a band of red paint across his forehead and a white
strip about his mouth. His only garment was a large guanaco skin thrown over the shoulder. The officers offered the
savages lengths of red cloth, which they promptly put
around their necks. With this gesture their distrustful expression gave way to one of friendliness. They patted the
white men's breasts, making a clucking noise such as people
use to call chickens. The leader then bared his bosom for
Darwin to return the compliment of chest-slapping.

Their language was gutteral and reminded him of Captain Cook's description—like a man clearing his throat.

Mostly, the Fuegians were interested in getting knives and conveyed the idea by imitating cutting movements on a piece of blubber. They were excellent mimics and aped everything the officers did—coughing, yawning, and making hideous faces. They recognized what guns were and showed great fear of them.

Jemmy Button came along with the party and he was immediately recognized by the Fuegians as one of them. In their clucking and clicking language they invited him to stay. But because they were of another tribe, Jemmy didn't understand their language. His own people were further along the coast.

The Fuegians' way of life was even more primitive than their dress. Their food consisted of limpets scraped from rocks, mussels, seals, and a few birds. The guanaco was hunted for food and skins. Their only property seemed to be bows and arrows and spears. Their constant search for food in this desolate, rocky country made nomadic life necessary and they had no permanent shelters. At their stopping places, they merely threw together a makeshift wigwam, shaped like a low haystack. It was made of branches and thatched roughly with grass and rushes—the barest possible shelter.

Though there was almost no level land and the hills were so thickly wooded as to seem impassable, Darwin was determined to explore this strange land. The trees were so close together and the branches so low, that he found it difficult to push through. Crawling up beside a mountain stream, he finally reached a height where the antarctic beech grew. In the still solitude of this little forest, he had the thrill of being the first civilized man to see it.

Thinking that the higher he climbed, the easier the walking would be, he was much disappointed to find that what had looked from below like a cover of green turf, was a compact mass of beech trees. Stunted by strong winds, they grew only four or five feet high, and their twisted branches hugged the ground. He was forced to walk on top of this mass, until he found a well-beaten path made by the guanacos. He came upon two of them, who cantered away, neighing like colts.

After several hours, he reached the peak and got a superb view of the sea, which well repaid his efforts. He collected some alpine flowers, the tiniest he had ever seen.

A few days later, the *Beagle* got under way, bound for Cape Horn, the terror of all mariners. The Horn "demanded his tribute & by night sent us a gale right in our teeth." They had to retreat, but two days later struggled back and saw "this notorious promontory in its proper form—veiled in a mist, and its dim outline surrounded by a storm of wind and water." Violent squalls drove them into Wigwam Cove and in this snug little harbor they celebrated Christmas as best they could.

Darwin and Sulivan climbed a nearby peak, thick with antarctic beech. They fired guns into caverns where wild fowl lived, yelled into them to get echoes, pounded the rocks with geological hammers, and amused themselves rolling huge stones down the precipice, all in full view of a group of Fuegians who must have thought them to be "the powers of darkness."

They spent several weeks in this stormy area, knocking about in weather which the Captain considered the most severe he had ever seen. Reports came of two vessels being wrecked during this time. One of the *Beagle's* boats was cut away and smashed to bits by a huge sea. It filled their decks so deeply that if the *Beagle* had not been such a stout vessel with tackle in good condition, they would have been in distress. "A less gale has dismasted & foundered many a good ship," Darwin wrote. Though he was becoming hardened, he suffered from much seasickness during this stormy time.

Finally they found a good anchorage and the missionary and the three Fuegians were taken in a flotilla of boats to Jemmy Button's part of the coast. Jemmy's tribe recognized him, but since he had forgotten his language and was dressed in clothes of the white man, they paid no attention to him and were more interested in begging for knives. When Jemmy's mother and brothers arrived, there was no demonstration of affection. They merely stared at him and then went off to see to their canoe. Darwin thought they displayed less emotion than horses meeting in a pasture.

The two other Fuegians, the man called York Minster after a local mountain and the girl, Fuegia Basket, were set on shore with the missionary Matthews, who had received many presents from the Missionary Society. But of what use were wine glasses, tea trays, soup tureens, mahogany dressing case, fine white linen and beaver hats?

Captain Fitzroy had his men dig gardens and build some wigwams for Matthews and the Fuegians. Then with Darwin and a few men, the Captain set out in two boats for a surveying cruise. When they returned three weeks later they found everything in ruins. Matthews' belongings were plundered and his life was threatened. There was reason to believe that the Fuegians were cannibals. Jemmy Button had told them that they ate their old women, something to which Darwin's party at first gave no credence. But it was reported that another Fuegian boy had told a sealing captain the same thing. When he was asked, "Why no eat dogs?" the boy answered, "Dog catch otter. Woman good for nothing. Man very hungry."

Evidently the *Beagle* had arrived just in time to save the missionary's life and he was taken aboard again to join a missionary brother in New Zealand. The three Fuegians who had had a taste of civilization decided to stay. Jemmy had already acquired a wife, although he had lost all his English finery. Jemmy's own brother had been stealing from him. Jemmy said, "What fashion you call that!" But he stayed, nevertheless. So ended the attempt of Captain Fitzroy to bring civilization to Tierra del Fuego!

Darwin commented, "It was quite melancholy leaving our Fuegians amongst their barbarous countrymen. There was one comfort; they appeared to have no personal fears." He was sure that the three years among Europeans had not changed them—or even been of any use to them.

In March, they reached the Falkland Islands, where the Captain planned to make an extensive survey, since it was important to whalers. There he purchased a large schooner, the *Adventure*, for use as supply ship, to spare the *Beagle* from running back and forth to shore. Wickham was put in command. All this was done on his own responsibility.

On the barren islands, Darwin saw some interesting animals: the now extinct wolf-like fox which hunted wild horses and rabbits, and the jackass penguin which brays like a donkey and uses its wings like front feet on land and as fins at sea. Another curious bird, flightless like the penguin, was the loggerhead duck or goose, sometimes also called the racehorse or steamer. Unable to fly, this duck uses its stumpy wings as paddles, *running* on the surface of the water, splashing but not submerging. "Thus we find in South America three birds which use their wings for other purposes besides flight, the penguin as fins, the Logger Duck as paddles, and the ostrich as sails," he wrote in the *Journal*. That was after he had seen the ostrich on the pampas, literally spreading its wings like taut sails and thus outdistancing gauchos galloping after them.

By April, the *Beagle* and *Adventure* were in the great estuary of the Rio Plata, with Buenos Aires and Montevideo on either side. Captain Fitzroy would be busy for some time refitting his ships and making surveys in the region, which gave Darwin a chance to live ashore. Except for short intervals when he rejoined the brig, he spent the next year on land, filling out his collections and riding over the pampas of Argentina with the gauchos—an extremely interesting species of genus homo.

For ten weeks he stayed at the town of Maldonado, east of Montevideo, and in that time made an almost perfect collection: several quadrupeds, eighty kinds of birds, and many reptiles, including nine species of snakes. He found eight varieties of mice in the region. His whole South American collection of mice finally amounted to twenty-seven species, nearly all that existed.

During this time, he made an excursion to the north in Uruguay, prudently hiring two guides and a string of horses. His guides were armed with pistols and sabres, "a precaution which I thought rather unnecessary; but the first piece of news we heard was, that the day before a traveller from Monte Video had been found dead on the road, with his throat cut. This happened close to a cross, the record of a former murder."

However, they met with nothing but hospitality along the road and Darwin was fascinated by the gauchos. Their name meant simply men of the pampas but they were a special breed: tall, handsome, with long black hair curling down their backs. They wore brightly colored clothes, great clanking spurs, and carried daggers at their waists. They were excessively polite—but quite ready to cut your throat if you displeased them.

On horseback, they carried a lasso of braided rawhide and it was a wonderful sight to see them whirling the noose around their head and then roping a cow with it. The *bolas*, or balls, was even more ingenious, Darwin thought. This weapon was simply three round stones covered with leather, strung on stout cords about eight feet long. "The Gaucho holds the smallest of the three in his hand, and whirls the other two round and round his head; then, taking aim, sends them like a chain shot revolving through the air. The balls no sooner strike any object than, winding round it, they cross each other, and become firmly hitched." The trick in using the *bolas* was to send the balls whirling around the quarry's neck when riding at a full gallop. When Darwin first practiced the art, he managed to foul the *bolas* around his horse's hind leg and the gauchos roared with laughter. But he learned.

During these weeks he became such a "complete landsman" that when, late in June, he boarded the *Beagle* with his menagerie, he bumped his head against the low decks and was uncomfortably conscious of the brig's roll while they were still in the harbor.

The *Beagle* was southbound and dropped Darwin off at the mouth of the Rio Negro, about three hundred miles below the Plata estuary. His next rendezvous with the brig would be back at the Plata; he would work his way northward through a wild country with no towns whatever. Moreover, he was to travel through terrain where General Rosas, soon to become dictator of Argentina, was carrying on a war of extermination against the Indians. They were on their ancestral lands, which the Spanish coveted; the simplest thing was to kill them off.

The only benefit of this military invasion, as far as Darwin was concerned, was the fact that General Rosas had established a chain of *postas* all the way north, where a change of horses could be had. He started off with a guide, an English trader called Harris, and five gauchos. They rode all day through desert country. That night was the first he had spent under the open sky of the pampas and he never forgot it. The gauchos found a stray cow, roped her, and in no time their supper was roasting over the fire. "Beef on the hide" was a gaucho specialty. They would hack off a choice steak, skin and all, and roast it with the tough hide next the flames, the edges turning up with the heat so that no juices were lost. After the feast, they bedded down around the fire on their saddles and slept in "the death-like stillness of the plain."

There was little naturalizing to be done on this long ride north, but Darwin had his fill of the brutal war against the Indians. He saw enough of these plains Indians to realize how little they resembled the wretched Fuegians and how like they were to the gauchos in pride and magnificent horsemanship. The idea was growing in his mind that people, like all living things, adapt to their environment and thus in some mysterious way are changed. Indians and gauchos were the copper and white varieties of men who belonged perfectly on the pampas. But he learned that the Indians had been there from very ancient times and this made their systematic extinction by the whites even more atrocious.

Finally, back at his old diggings near Bahia Blanca, Darwin found additional fossils and bones of animals even more ancient than the Indians. The *Beagle* was anchored offshore and he packed up crates of his findings to send Henslow. He hired his cabin boy, Covington, to shoot and skin birds and himself made two expeditions north to collect the last specimens from Uruguay and upper Argentina. Exhausted and half-ill from constant overwork, he was glad to be back on the *Beagle*. She left the Plata on December 6, "never again to enter its muddy stream."

9

Patagonia

JUST BEFORE CHRISTMAS, the *Beagle* anchored off southern Argentina, not far above Tierra del Fuego. Later the expedition made one more trip to that dreary land where Jemmy Button, thin as a scarecrow, was bravely struggling to survive; and one more trip to the Falklands. To Darwin the exciting part of these months was the exploration of Patagonia, the desert plains below the pampas. The excitement was almost altogether caused by the geology of the region, which told a story as startling as anything in the first two volumes of Lyell, which by now he had received and absorbed.

As always, he observed everything around him with great care before he allowed himself to speculate about causes. He found that the plains rose above the coast in a series of steps, each a few feet higher than the other. The treeless cliffs, covered only with thorny shrubs and wiry grass, held innumerable shells and fossilized bones. The stream beds were dry and supported only occasional stunted trees. "A man might walk for days together over these plains without finding a single drop of water," Darwin said. The heat was so great that the landscape seemed to tremble with the heat waves, causing mirages. Occasionally, his party would meet hunters in search of the wild guanaco, the only large animal of the region. His companions thought the country most dreary but to Darwin it had a fascination.

He saw that the surface gravel was made up of smooth rounded pebbles. This must mean that they had been smoothed by repeated action of breakers. The marine shells embedded in the rock were both recent, like the ones on the beach, and extinct—farther inland. He decided that the land had risen in several stages and had become terraced as the sea receded.

The guanacos, though wild, exhibited a strange curiosity toward people. Darwin and his companions soon discovered that they were intrigued by any motion—the lifting of an arm, kicking of the legs, or other antics. In this way, they enticed these strange beasts to come quite close to them.

How did these animals survive in this desolate barren country with only foul and salty water in the pools here and there? The answer was soon apparent as they came upon guanacos drinking this saline water and swimming from island to island in the brackish river mouths. Darwin found piles of guanaco bones and skulls bleached by the sun but without any signs of having been gnawed. This meant that there were no meat-eating animals on the plains. Alone adapted to drinking salt water, the guanaco held sway with little danger of a natural enemy.

Traveling farther south, Darwin came across fossils which seemed to be the ancestors of the living animals. Though larger, they were simpler than their descendants. Could these extinct animals in turn have come from still simpler forms, he wondered? If that were so, it should be possible to trace the succession of types showing gradual changes from the earliest to the present forms. Would this not prove that new forms *evolved* and were not *created* as we see them today?

With every new discovery, Darwin came closer to the conviction that living creatures must have developed from simpler ancestors.

In April, after visiting Tierra del Fuego and the Falklands, the *Beagle* returned to Patagonia. During the previous survey, Captain Fitzroy had traveled up the Santa Cruz River for a thirty-mile stretch but lack of provisions had forced him to return. This time he was determined to travel all the way to its source to see if it was navigable up to the Cordilleras (the Spanish name for the Andes). In three whaleboats, they stocked provisions for three weeks and twenty-five men, including Darwin, started out in the spring of 1834.

Pulling against the powerful river current made the going upstream slow and difficult. The trip was taking longer than they had expected. They fastened the three boats head to stern, left two men in each to steer, while the rest climbed up the rocky river banks pulling the boats with a tracking line. The party was divided into two watches, the men on the banks taking turns every hour and a half, hauling at the tracking line.

After sunset, the first level spot was chosen for the night's lodging. Navy rules were shelved on this expedition. The officers of each boat lived with, ate the same food, and slept in the same tents with their crew. Each man took his turn at cooking. Some hauled the boat to shore, while the cook made the fire. Others pitched the tent, the rest collected firewood and carried supplies from the boat. A watch of two men looked after the boats, kept up the fire, and stood guard against the Indians. Each man took an hour's watch every night.

The days were unbearably hot and the nights bitter cold. Long treks inland under the scorching sun with little chance of finding water on the way meant that they had to conserve what they carried in their flasks. And their food was beginning to give out. It was a severe trial of a man's endurance to ration the dwindling supply of bread and water.

Darwin had learned that drinking a little now and then made one feel the thirst all the more, and so he trained himself to drink once in the morning and not again until evening. Once on a hot day when, with a group of surveyors, he walked some fifteen miles, they were astonished at his endurance and toughness in the face of hunger and thirst. So this was the man whose nose betrayed weakness about which the Captain had had misgivings back home!

On the eighth day of the climb toward the Andes, Darwin found the change he was looking for. The mountains themselves were muffled in a heavy bank of clouds, but they were sending an occasional tree-trunk or a boulder of basaltic rock down the river. The bed of the river had been gravel, now it contained pebbles of basaltic rock. Soon they saw, a few miles ahead, a great platform of basalt from which these pebbles had come. The little stones became larger and larger until they were immense boulders. As they knew only too well, the Santa Cruz had a tremendously strong current and yet it had been unable to carry these great rocks more than three or four miles below the platform from which they had split off. This proved Darwin said, "the inefficiency of rivers in transporting even moderately-sized fragments.

"The basalt is only lava, which has flowed beneath the sea," his notes went on, "but the eruptions must have been on the grandest scale." For the great platform which they soon reached was a titanic mass which had originally been part of the Cordillera. "What power, then, has removed along a whole line of country, a solid mass of very hard rock?" Not the river, not even a great flood. No, this valley must once have been an arm of the sea. "If I had space I could prove that South America was formerly here cut off by a strait, joining the Atlantic and Pacific oceans, like that of Magellan."

Then this strait, with its sea shells, had gradually risen, a bit at a time, which explained the terraces along the coast and along the Santa Cruz. And the mountain flanks, "undermined by the water of this ancient strait, were broken up into huge fragments." Darwin admitted it made him giddy to think what ages it had taken to produce this change but he could not agree with geologists who thought such effects were produced by a sudden violent disaster. "No possible action of any flood could thus have modelled the land," he insisted.

The day after this tremendous conviction was reached, Darwin shot a condor measuring eight and a half feet from tip to tip of the wings. This mighty bird of the Andes was in line with his exalted mood. Then, to his joy, he found some plants he had seen nowhere else—except on the other side of this ancient strait in Tierra del Fuego. Despite the tremendous upheavals and the ages which had separated them, these humble little plants had somehow survived— their existence here helped Charles Darwin prove a theory.

Seeing the white summits of the Andes two days later was almost an anticlimax. Heavy clouds still hung about the peaks and the going got more and more difficult. They were on a half allowance of bread, which was not enough for men making a hard day's march.

On May 4, when they were one hundred and forty miles from the Atlantic and only sixty from the nearest arm of the Pacific, Captain Fitzroy called a halt. They got into the boats and shot down the river, up which they had toiled for eighteen days, in the short space of three. Only to Darwin had the expedition been worth while.

The facts were piling up and Darwin was slowly hammering out the answers to his many questions. But he would have to get back to England, to talk with the "authorities" before he could be sure. Captain Fitzroy, facing the same facts, saw them with different eyes. More firmly than ever, he believed that the present species had been created anew, as was described in the Bible. There was no meeting ground between the developing geologist-naturalist and his commanding officer who was trying to fit the facts into his fixed notion of Special Creation.

10

Earthquakes and Volcanoes

Late in May 1834, the *Beagle* and the *Adventure* anchored at Port Famine, so-called because a couple of centuries earlier the Spanish had abandoned it for lack of food. They were preparing for the passage to the west coast, through Magellan Strait. On the way they would get a glimpse of Tierra del Fuego in "her white drapery," for the antarctic winter was approaching. While Fitzroy was anxious to see the Magdalen Channel, a newly opened passage to the west, for Darwin the special attraction was to be Mount Sarmiento, one of the highest mountains of the Cape Horn region.

Darwin again was delighted with news from home and replied: "Continue in your good custom of writing plenty of gossip, I much like hearing all about all things. Remember me most kindly to Uncle Jos and to all the Wedgwoods . . . I have not forgotten the comfort I received that day at Maer, when my mind was like a swinging Pendulum.

"Give my best love to my Father. I hope he will forgive all my extravagance . . ." Should they all wonder what he looked like, he added that they would be amused with his "great beard." One of the treasures in this last mail was the arrival, at a most appropriate moment, of the third volume of Lyell's book.

Early in June, just before they entered the Pacific, Sarmiento with its twin snow-covered peaks was in full view. What luck! For it was usually cloaked in mist. Outlined against a blue sky, its dazzling white summit made an unforgettable impression on the *Beagle* voyagers. Its enormous mass of everlasting snow would stay as long as the "world holds together," Darwin reflected. By night, they reached the western part of the Channel but the water was too deep for anchoring. The ship had to stand off and on for fourteen hours in the pitch darkness and once got very near the rocks. This was one night when the Captain and the officers were really anxious about the little ship's safety.

Before they dropped anchor at the island of Chiloe, in the Pacific, Mr. Rowlett, the purser, died. Only thirty-eight, he was the oldest officer on board and warmly respected by them all. The funeral service was read on the quarter-deck and his body lowered into the sea. ". . . it is an aweful & solemn sound, that splash of the waters over the body of an old ship-mate."

The scenery was beginning to take on a tropical look—tall bamboo grass, large ferns, and thick woods which reminded Darwin of Brazil. But the incessant rain of the winter season on the island made them all happy to be on their way.

By the end of July, after a succession of northern gales, they reached Valparaiso, the Valley of Paradise. The climate was "quite delicious:" the sky clear and blue, "the air so dry & the sun so bright, that all nature seemed sparkling with life." The low white houses of the town built at the foot of the mountains recalled Teneriffe. To the northeast, Darwin caught glimpses of the Andes. The volcano of Aconcagua, rising to 23,000 feet, was especially beautiful.

He was pleasantly surprised by the number of well-educated English residents in the city—people who had read works on geology and other sciences. He was even asked what he thought of Lyell's book. It was good to find people who "actually take an interest in subjects no way connected with bales of goods & pounds, shillings & pence." Valparaiso was a small London or Paris, very different from the cities on the east coast. Except for the annoyance of having to shave and dress formally, he would enjoy his stay among these friendly people.

Good news was awaiting him from England. His father liked his *Journal* and didn't think him extravagant for hiring a servant to help with his collecting; in fact, he was relieved to know Charles had a companion in places where it was dangerous to travel alone. All his sisters had written too and sent packages, a box of books and a chain from Caroline on which to hang his pencil case. The shoes they sent were invaluable. Best of all, there was a letter from Henslow which had been a year and a half in transit, arriving long after other letters from his friend. Darwin had been worried that perhaps the specimens he had sent Henslow had been too poor to be acknowledged. To his delight, Henslow assured him they were a splendid contribution to science.

A special surprise was discovering an old school friend from Shrewsbury, Richard Corfield, who invited Darwin to stay at his house near the city. One story high, all its rooms opened on a patio with a small garden. Corfield knew the country well; he had several horses and gave Darwin much help in his geological excursions. He arranged for two *guasos*, the Chilean version of the gaucho, to act as Darwin's guides.

For the first few weeks, Darwin explored the nearby region, then took longer trips on horseback up the poor mountain paths. Always eager to climb peaks, he and his *guasos* set out one day for the summit of the Campaña, or Bell Mountain, 6400 feet high. Toward evening they unsaddled their horses beside a spring and camped out. Building a fire beneath a shelter of bamboos, they fried their jerked beef. Their drink was maté, the tea of South America. He enjoyed life in the open, with the quiet broken only by the shrill noise of the mountain bizcatcha and the cry of the goatsucker.

The next morning they reached the summit, crowned by a rough mass of greenstone. He spent the whole day on the peak, for all Chile, with the Andes and the Pacific, lay below him like a relief map.

He wondered at "the force which has upheaved these mountains, and . . . the countless ages which it must have required, to have broken through, removed, and levelled whole masses of them." Recalling the vast sedimentary beds of Patagonia which were once part of the Cordilleras, then higher by many thousand feet, he wondered how any mountain chain could have supplied such masses without being themselves obliterated. Now if you "reverse the wonder," what vast eons of time it would take to grind down the gigantic Cordillera into the gravel and mud of Patagonia! It was all part of one continuous process of violent upheavals, followed by an unending wearing down of mammoth mountains, piling up the vast wastes of debris below.

Sitting around the fire with the *guasos*, he could not help contrasting them with the gauchos of the pampas. The gaucho might be a cutthroat but he was a gentleman, while the *guaso* was downtrodden and ordinary. He had none of the elegance of the gaucho in manners or dress. In fact, he stood pretty low in the sharply marked class distinctions of Chile. The country was in some ways more civilized than Argentina, but Darwin's family tradition of humanity made him dislike the Chilean system of rich men who owned the land and the mines, and poor men like his *guasos* who slaved for pitiful wages.

He visited gold and copper mines and was shocked at what he saw. There was no machinery to lighten the work, as in England. Instead of pumping water seepage from the shafts, the men actually scooped up the water and carried it to the surface in leather bags. From a depth of four hundred and fifty feet, they climbed up notched tree trunks that served as ladders, carrying burdens of two hundred pounds. Men and boys worked from dawn until dark for miserable pay and just enough food to keep them going. All the workers, in the mines or on the land, were half-starved and lived on little but beans.

Circling through the Andes, he stopped at towns and villages where even the upper-class Spanish had none of the polish of Valparaiso. In one town, an old Spanish lawyer was asked what he thought about the King of England sending a naturalist to their country to break rocks and collect lizards and beetles. The lawyer answered that it looked suspicious—"No man," he declared, "is so rich as to send out people to pick up such rubbish; I do not like it."

Toward the end of September, Darwin was on his way back to Valparaiso, when he became ill. With great difficulty he managed to get back to Corfield's house, where he remained in bed for a month. His illness was never diagnosed, but it was serious and drained his energies. Lying helpless, he fretted at this frustration in his collecting.

During his illness the expedition itself was threatened. Fitzroy had been ordered by the Admiralty to sell the *Ad-*

venture, though he had paid for the vessel out of his own funds and wished to have the Admiralty pay only for the keep of the crew. This was such a blow that Fitzroy threatened to resign. He was on the edge of a nervous collapse. Finally, the officers persuaded him to stay in command but to cut the voyage short. It had already lasted much longer than they had planned.

All this delayed their sailing south to the islands of Chiloe and Chonos so that Darwin was well enough to go along. Dreary as these islands were, he found much of interest and was delighted when a long dormant volcano suddenly erupted, as if for his benefit. He watched the magnificent spectacle from a distance, standing on the *Beagle's* deck with a spyglass most of the night. By morning all was quiet. What really astonished him was to hear later that a volcano five hundred miles away in Chile had erupted the same night and another, 2700 miles farther north, had gone into terrific activity, accompanied by an earthquake six hours later. Was this a coincidence or was there some subterranean connection? All three volcanos belonged to the same mountain chain.

In February, 1835, the *Beagle* sailed north again, stopping for a survey at Valdivia. A week later a severe earthquake shook all southern Chile. At Valdivia, they escaped the full force of the quake but Darwin was profoundly impressed.

> This day has been memorable in the annals of Valdivia . . . I was on shore & lying down in the wood to rest myself. It came on suddenly & lasted two minutes, but the time appeared much longer. The rocking of the ground was most sensible . . . the motion made me almost giddy.
>
> A bad earthquake at once destroys our oldest associations; the earth, the very emblem of solidity, has moved beneath our feet like a thin crust over a fluid.

Valdivia had suffered only a severe shake-up but Concepción, which they soon visited, was wrecked completely. There, not a house was left standing. The city had become mere piles of brick, tile, and timbers. The cathedral was in ruins. Its solid buttresses, six to ten feet thick, had crumbled like so much biscuit. Fortunately, the earthquake had come just before noon, when the people were awake and out of their houses. Had the quake occurred at night, many thousands would have perished.

Concepción was the center of the quake, which was felt for four hundred miles along the coast. It was the greatest earthquake in the memory of the oldest men. The immensity of desolation that it produced in a matter of minutes! Near Concepción the ocean rose and a colossal tidal wave swept over the lowland, lifting the buildings from their foundations. Receding with almost the same force, it washed the remnants of buildings and drowned cattle in the sea. Ships which had been in the harbor were driven far inland and left high and dry.

Darwin went about studying the ruins. From the resistance offered by the cathedral walls which remained standing and the direction of fall of the tumbled ones, he calculated that the disturbance had come from the southwest. He noted also the effect on water springs. Some had become closed over by the shift of the earth's crust, others poured forth more water than usual. From some, hot black fluid with bubbles of gas flowed.

He was excited to learn that volcanic action had accompanied the earthquake. Several volcanoes on Chiloe erupted violently and continued active for a long time, an undersea volcano near the island of Juan Fernández, three hundred and sixty miles to the northeast, burst forth. He found evidence of an undersea lake of lava, seven hundred and twenty miles long and four hundred wide, twice as big as the Black Sea, which from time to time produced both eruptions and earthquakes that affected this whole area. The earth, as he himself had experienced, was a mere crust over a fluid, melted mass of rock and volcanoes are openings through this crust. If the volcanic action is violent enough, the black lava gas escapes through other openings such as water springs. "The Earthquake & Volcano are parts of one of the greatest phenomena to which this world is subject," he recorded in his diary.

Most remarkable of all, was the confirmation, before his very eyes, of the theory of elevation and subsidence. The land around the Bay of Concepción was raised two or three feet. At the island of Santa Maria about thirty miles southeast, the elevation was even greater. There Captain Fitzroy found beds of putrid mussel shells still clinging to the rocks, ten feet above the high-water mark; before the earthquake, the inhabitants had dived at low water for these shells. It was hardly possible to doubt that the shells he had found at an elevation of 1300 feet near Valparaiso revealed a long history of "successive small uprisings, such as that which accompanied or caused the earthquake of this year . . ." Soon Darwin was to find even more striking evidence of the forces which had shaped and were still shaping the earth, as Lyell too believed.

One last adventure lay ahead—crossing the Andes. There were two passes in southern Chile which cut through the Cordillera and it was characteristic that Darwin chose the higher and more dangerous one, the Portillo.

He took along one of his old *guasos* and a driver for their ten mules. A string of mules always had a *madrina* or godmother—a steady old mare which they followed obediently. The devoted attachment of the mules to the *madrina* saved a great deal of trouble. Four of the beasts carried the party's supplies and if they had strayed off, disaster would have followed. It was March and they were approaching the winter season, an especially risky time to cross the Portillo.

As they climbed, Darwin listened to the roar of the mountain torrents. "The sound spoke eloquently to the geologist; the thousands and thousands of stones, which, striking against each other, made the one dull uniform sound, were hurrying in one direction,"—to the sea Darwin noted. He now understood how, over untold ages, this relentless force could wear down mountains and deposit layers of debris which built up the plains below.

Now that Darwin had accepted Lyell's vast geological time scale, he traveled among wonders. There was the wild music of the torrents which wore down mountains and the violence of past upheavals, of which he had just seen the latest one, forever pushing the land and its mountains up above the sea. The cycles were clear to him: the upward push by volcanoes, followed by a period of wearing down. He could actually count these cycles by counting the terraces of debris. "No one fact in the geology of South America interested me more than these terraces of rudely-stratified shingle," he wrote.

Their path lay across two ranges, the Peuqueñes, which they crossed at roughly 13,000 feet, and then the Portillo range, a thousand feet higher. On both he found fossil shells. It was wonderful to think that these lofty ridges, where men and mules labored for breath, had once lain at the bottom of the sea. And even more incredible was the thought that the crests had once been thousands of feet higher and had been slowly whittled down by the labor of the elements.

There was perpetual snow at the top of the Peuqueñes and more would fall soon. There was a cutting wind from the Pacific. But Darwin held in his hands shells of animals which had once crawled on the bottom of the Pacific and, looking back at Chile where he had learned nature's secrets in one of her most unguarded moments, he was filled with awe. "I felt glad that I was alone," he wrote.

After they crossed the Peuqueñes, they descended to a saddle between the two ranges, where the elevation was still about 11,000 feet. Here they camped for the night. Vegetation was scanty and the only fuel available was the root of a small, scrubby plant; the fire was miserably low and the wind piercingly cold. The next morning they tried to cook potatoes but, at this low atmospheric pressure, water boiled so slowly that after several hours the potatoes remained uncooked. His companions cursed the pot because it "did not choose to boil potatoes."

Reaching the top of the Portillo after a laborious climb, they saw clear across the vast plains to the Atlantic. The brilliant sun and the clear air brought the rivers into full view, glistening like silver threads till they were lost in the great distance. The view was more inspiring than the plain of Mendoza, down to which they now came. It was "devoid of all interest," Darwin declared, a remarkable statement from this man who found so much to fascinate him.

They returned to Chile by the lower and safer Uspallata pass and there, he made a miraculous find. At an elevation of 7000 feet, Darwin found snow-white columns projecting from a bare slope. They were petrified trees, a whole little forest of fifty or more, abruptly broken off, the upright stumps projecting a few feet above the ground. The trunks measured three to five feet around. The stone still retained the impression of the bark.

"It required little geological practice to interpret the marvelous story which this scene at once unfolded; though I confess I was so much astonished, that I could scarcely believe the plainest evidence."

He imagined these stumps once alive with green leaves on the shores of the Atlantic, now driven back seven hundred miles, but which had once reached clear to the foot of the Andes. The trees had grown from a volcanic soil that had been raised above the sea bottom. Then these trees had been submerged beneath the ocean, as the shore slowly sank again. There they were covered with layers of sediment and later by enormous streams of submarine lava. Once more the subterranean forces thrust upward a chain of mountains and Darwin was now viewing the transformed trees, their living cells converted into silex.

From the layers of sand and lava, and sand and lava again, he read the story of "deluges of molten stone and aqueous deposits five times alternately . . . spread out." The slow but unending erosive work of wind, rain, and snow went on, until the stony stumps were bared—witnesses to nature's "vast, and scarcely comprehensible" changes.

These changes, he declared, were recent compared with the history of the Cordillera, which itself was "absolutely modern" compared with the fossil-bearing layers of Europe. While he was sure of his conclusions, he hardly expected to be believed at home and so he collected "a half a mule's load" of specimens to send Henslow.

Back in Valparaiso, Darwin wrote Susan, "Since leaving England I have never made so successful a journey; it has, however, been very expensive. I am sure my Father would not regret it, if he could know how deeply I have enjoyed it . . . I cannot express the delight which I felt at such a famous winding up of all my Geology in South America."

During the next four months while the *Beagle* was surveying the northern coast of Chile and then Peru, Darwin's thoughts were increasingly bent on home. South America had turned a naturalist into a geologist and he was almost surfeited with the marvels he had seen. When, on September 7, 1835, the *Beagle* set sail, he had no premonition that the crowning revelation was still to come.

I I

Islands of the Giant Tortoise

HEADING NORTHWEST from Peru, the towering Andes to starboard, they set sail for the first group of Pacific islands, the Galapagos. Discovered by the Spanish in the seventeenth century, the islands were owned by the Republic of Ecuador. Little was known about this curious archipelago lying below the equator five or six hundred miles off the west coast of South America. About the only travelers who visited the bleak Galapagos were whalers, sealers, and buccaneers who stopped to replenish their supplies.

Chatham Island (now called San Cristobal), the easternmost of the group, had been partially surveyed by Captain Collnett many years before and, with the help of his charts, Fitzroy was able to locate it. The *Beagle* crew were the first real explorers here and Darwin was the first to study the islands with the eyes of a scientist.

Despite their closeness to the equator, the climate of the Galapagos was not tropical, since they lay in the cold waters of the great southern polar current. The lower parts of the islands were dry and sterile but the higher parts caught the rain and were greener.

On the morning of the 17th of September, when they landed on Chatham Island, it seemed to Darwin that no place could have been less inviting than this volcanic dump heap of lava and old craters. The parched surface, heated by the noonday sun, felt like a hot stove underfoot. The black lava fields were everywhere covered with stunted, sun-scorched brushwood. It was a disappointing sight for the collector. The wretched looking weeds, Darwin thought, would have better suited the Arctic than an equatorial island.

While the *Beagle* sailed around Chatham Island, anchoring successively in several bays, Darwin camped on shore. The first morning, as he was scrambling over the jagged surface of the lava plain, he came on an astonishing sight. There were two giant armored tortoises—*galapagos*—from which the islands got their Spanish name. Each must have weighed about two hundred pounds. One was munching on a piece of cactus but slowly stalked away as it discovered him approaching; the other greeted him with a deep hiss and drew in its head.

These huge reptiles surrounded by black lava, leafless shrubs, and large cacti, were, he fancied, "like some antediluvian animals." Strange creatures found in no other part of the globe, they struck him as very ancient, as if they had been there before Noah's flood. They should long ago have become extinct, laid down in the rocks as fossils—but here they were, still alive. It was as if nature had stopped short with the production of these curious beasts and not kept step with the rest of the world. Stranger yet that so many of them should be found only on this little group of islands in the middle of the ocean!

Though their numbers had been much reduced by ships' crews who captured them for food, they were still abundant, he soon learned. Tales were told of a ship taking seven hundred of them at one time. In one day the *Beagle* crew caught fifteen. Since the tortoises lived on succulent cacti, a bundle of these plants was taken on board to feed them until they were killed off as needed. Some yielded as much as two hundred pounds of delicious meat. It took six or eight men to lift the heavier ones, which might weigh up to four hundred pounds.

In his usual systematic way, Darwin studied the habits of these reptiles on the various islands. While they could live on the low arid plains, they made well-beaten roads to the high, damper places for leaves and berries and especially for water. They were prodigious drinkers. Following one of them on its path up to the springs, Darwin watched it bury its head in the water, swallowing great mouthfuls, at the rate of ten a minute. He learned that the tortoises usually remained in these watering places for three or four days, drinking and wallowing in the mud. After such a visit, their bladders were distended with fluid, a reserve supply for the time spent in the dry places.

Night and day they traveled, lumberingly and persistently. Like the tortoise in the tale, they slowly but surely made headway. One, that he timed, walked at the rate of sixty yards in ten minutes, 360 yards an hour, four miles a day.

Darwin heard that the tortoise was deaf but he decided to find out for himself. Walking close behind one, he found that his steps were not heard but was amused to discover that the instant he overtook the crawling giant, it would draw in head and legs, utter a deep hiss, and fall to the ground with a heavy thud, as if struck dead. He frequently got on the back of one, giving a few raps on the hind part of the shell; the reptile would rise and walk away but its rider would soon lose his balance and slide off.

As it happened, Darwin's stay on the islands was at the

mating season in October. During breeding time, the hoarse roar of the male could be heard more than a hundred yards away. The females laid their eggs in the sandy soil; or where the ground was rocky dropped them carelessly in any depression. Darwin examined some of the round white eggs which measured over seven inches in circumference.

The turtle was not the only aboriginal creature on the islands. There were also certain lizards found nowhere else. There were two species, an aquatic variety and a land dweller. The water lizard, a hideous creature, dirty black, "stupid, and sluggish in its movements," might be three or four feet long and weigh twenty pounds. Occasionally, he saw them on the rocky beaches but most of the time they were swimming.

Captain Collnett had reported that these lizards went to sea in "herds a-fishing" and only sunned themselves on the rocks. But did they really live on fish? The naturalist took nothing for granted. Opening the stomachs of several, he found them full of minced seaweed such as grew on the ocean bottom. Their large, pouched intestines, characteristic of herbivorous animals, gave further proof that they were plant-eaters.

And certainly they were aquatic, though with an odd "fear" of the sea. If anything frightened them, they took refuge on the shore. He found that they would sooner allow him to hold them by the tail than jump into the water.

He threw a lizard into a tidal pool and saw it make for shore in a beeline to where he stood, entering some crevice or hiding under a clump of seaweed. Each time he repeated this game, the animal hastily returned the same way. Apparently this lizard had no enemy on shore but, at sea, was prey to shark and other fish and so when it was frightened, sought safety on shore.

The land form had its own peculiar ways. Living in burrows, this ugly lizard dug its burrows everywhere in the lava or the soft sandstone. The soil over these burrows was constantly giving way underfoot—an annoyance to the tired walker.

Darwin watched them burrowing. One front leg scratched up the soil throwing it toward the hind foot, which was placed so as to flick the dirt beyond the mouth of the hole. When one side tired, the alternate legs took up the digging. He watched one at work until it was halfway in its hole, then he pulled it by the tail. "At this it was greatly astonished, and soon shuffled up to see what was the matter; and then stared me in the face, as much as to say, 'What made you pull my tail?'" Feeding by day, they didn't wander far from the burrows; when frightened they rushed to their hiding place.

These lizards, too, were plant-eating. Even the tiny birds accepted them as harmless. Darwin once saw a thick-billed finch picking at one end of a piece of cactus while a lizard was munching at the other. A few moments later the bird, with the utmost indifference, hopped on the back of the reptile. The lizards would often crawl up the trunks of the stunted acacia trees to get their leaves. The meat was considered a delicacy "by those whose stomachs soar above all prejudices."

Unlike any other part of the world, where mammals predominated, here the reptiles reigned supreme in their isolation. The only native mammal Darwin discovered was a mouse and this lived solely on Chatham Island.

His study of fossils had shown him that reptiles belonged to an age long before mammals developed. Except for the little mouse on Chatham, he was back somewhere in paleolithic times, observing a very early stage of life. Had the Special Creation in which Fitzroy—and indeed, most people —firmly believed, neglected the Galapagos since the Age of Reptiles? Were these strange islands simply a relic of that age, left unchanged for thousands of years?

Darwin's explanation was startling in its implications.

The archipelago is a little world within itself, or rather a satellite attached to America, whence it has derived a few stray colonists. . . . Considering the small size of these islands, we feel the more astonished at the number of their aboriginal beings, and at their confined range. Seeing every height crowned with its crater, [he wrote in his *Journal*] and the boundaries of most of the lava-streams still distinct, we are led to believe that within a period, geologically recent, the unbroken ocean was here spread out. Hence, both in space and time, we seem to be brought somewhat near to that great fact—that mystery of mysteries—the first appearance of new beings on this earth.

Wherever he turned, questions cropped up that he couldn't answer. The delight of finding new species was matched by the excitement of trying to explain them. What a rich corner of the earth these islands were for the collector! Fifteen kinds of sea fish—all new species; sixteen land shells, all but one peculiar to the archipelago; and twenty-six land birds to be found nowhere else. Even more remarkable was the fact that the species were different on the different islands.

On James Island (now called San Salvador), out of seventy-five plant species, thirty-eight grew only on the archipelago and thirty exclusively on that one island. On Albemarle Island (now called Isla Isabella), of twenty-six "aboriginal Galapageian" plants, twenty-two were confined to this one island. Of the two hundred and twenty-five different plants he collected, one hundred were new species. He was "surrounded by new birds, new reptiles, new shells, new insects, new plants."

Of all the birds, the finches interested him most. Thirteen

distinct species were closely related to each other and all were peculiar to the Galapagos. He observed that their beaks could be arranged in a perfectly graded series from a large parrot-like shape to tiny sharply pointed ones; in between there were curved, straight, flat, and blunt shapes. This fact led to another question. Could species somehow be modified, changed along a certain direction? "Seeing this gradation and diversity of structure in one small, intimately related group of birds, one might really fancy that from an original paucity of birds in this archipelago, one species had been taken and modified for different ends."

Tucked away in his notebook on birds was the statement that a further study of the Galapagos life "would undermine the stability of the Species." All too aware of the revolutionary meaning attached to such an idea, he did not risk publishing it in the *Journal.* He could not yet be sure of its absolute truth and such an idea would severely challenge the doctrine of Special Creation. Darwin was not yet ready for such a break, but what he had seen was slowly giving him an insight into the closest secrets of nature.

Everything he saw during the month or more that the *Beagle* remained in the Galapagos revealed their unique quality. Of his collection of insects which he ticketed with their location, not one was found on any two islands. So it was also with the thrushes. All those from Charles Island (now called Santa María), belonged to one species and those from Chatham and James Islands to another. How could so many varieties of plants and animals have been produced in this small part of the earth's surface?

On the other hand, there was the case of the waders and water birds. Only three of the eleven he found were new species. Compared with the land birds, the web-footed ones had a wider range, as in other parts of the world. Living on water, they were more mobile, which accounted for their wider distribution.

A chance remark by his host Mr. Lawson, the English Vice-Governor stationed on Charles Island, gave Darwin a clue to the peculiarity of the Galapagos creatures.

Lawson said, "You know, Mr. Darwin, I can tell at a glance which island a tortoise comes from."

At the moment, the remark did not register. Darwin had not noticed any differences and had already pooled his specimens from two of the islands. Then Lawson's remark sank in. He rushed back to the boat to see for himself. Sure enough, the tortoise shells from different islands were slightly different in shape, thickness, and color. The islanders told him that tortoises on certain islands had better-tasting meat than the others.

"I never dreamed that islands, about fifty or sixty miles apart, and most of them in sight of each other, formed of precisely the same rocks, placed under quite a similar climate, rising to nearly equal height, would have been differently tenanted," he confessed.

Had the voyage begun with the stop at the Galapagos, instead of the mainland, the full meaning of what Darwin saw might have escaped him. But arriving there after nearly four years of studying life on the continent, he already knew that land barriers had led to the development of different mammals in North and South America. Separation and isolation resulted in modifications.

Despite their closeness, the Galapagos were effectively separated from each other. Very strong currents, running in a westerly direction, cut off the northern from the southern islands. This made "transportal by sea" virtually impossible. The islands were also remarkably free of wind gales, so that birds, insects, and the lighter seeds could hardly be blown from one to the other. If seeds or eggs found their way to the ocean, they were more apt to be swept out to the open Pacific by the swift current than across to another island. Finally, Darwin said, the great depth of the ocean between the islands and their recent volcanic origin "rendered it highly unlikely that they were ever united."

The singular giant tortoises, the strange finches with their graded beaks, the aboriginal lizards, and the rare shells could be explained. Separation accounted for this distinctiveness.

The idea of changeability of species was beginning to take root in Darwin's mind. On these barren islands, he had found much exciting evidence of the endless cycles of change in living things. Without much more study he dared not put on paper or even share with anyone the upsetting idea of a gradual evolution of life. But Galapagos had shaken the accepted idea of stability of species.

On October 20, the *Beagle* set its course southwest for Tahiti. Before they would reach home there were still three oceans to cross. They would visit New Zealand and Australia, the Keeling (or Cocos) and Mauritius Islands in the Indian Ocean, then round Africa, stop at St. Helena and the Ascension Islands, go back for a last look at Bahia, and finally turn homewards. Writing to Caroline from New Zealand on December 27th, 1835, the fourth anniversary of his departure, Darwin expressed his yearnings for home.

> I count & recount every stage in the journey homewards, & an hour lost is reckoned of more consequence than a week formerly. There is no more Geology but plenty of sea-sickness; . . . Think & pity me. But everything is tolerable when I recollect that this day eight months I probably shall be sitting by your fireside.

Tahiti was already checked off the list. It had been charming, as promised. But Darwin was worn out with constant seasickness and the long journey down to New Zealand and Australia was an ordeal.

When at last they anchored in Sydney Cove on January 12, 1836, the many large ships in the harbor surrounded by warehouses, the windmills on the edge of the bank, the beautiful villas scattered along the beach, the stone houses two and three stories high told them they were in a populous city, the capital of New South Wales.

Walking through Sydney the first evening, Charles Darwin congratulated himself on being an Englishman. For here he saw the "most magnificent testimony to the power of the British nation." But his feeling of patriotic pride was short lived. The chain gang convict labor, the flogging of servants, the rapid extermination of the natives, the lack of culture all depressed him.

In his explorations, he found the country dull and uninviting and deplored the near extinction of the emu and the kangaroo. Still, there were memorable highlights: the eucalyptus forest, the luxuriant tree ferns and the duck-billed platypus. Like the giant tortoise in the Galapagos, this egg-laying mammal was a survivor of the distant past.

As they set their course for Keeling Island, he was glad to say farewell to Australia. "You are a rising child, and doubtless some day will reign a great princess in the South; but you are too great and ambitious for affection, yet not great enough for respect. I leave your shores without sorrow or regret."

On April 1, 1836, they reached Keeling, just south of Sumatra. This was one of the lagoon islands or atolls built by coral. Inside the ring-shaped atoll lay the lagoon, with its shallow, clear water, a vivid green under the vertical rays of the sun. The little ring of land separated the calm lagoon from the heaving water of the ocean and its snow-white breakers.

On the inner side of the lagoon, there was a beach of glistening white chalk and, on its ocean side, solid flat coral rock. The structure and origin of the coral islands held special fascination for Darwin and he had conceived a theory about them before he left South America.

He waded out to sea as far as the living mounds of coral that were constantly being battered by sea breakers. The force of the waves seemed invincible, "yet these low, insignificant coral islets stand and are victorious, for here another power . . . takes part in the contest." He was moved by the power of the tiny coral polyps to conquer brute force.

With Captain Fitzroy, Darwin rowed out about a mile from shore and dropped a sounding line 7200 feet long and still it didn't reach bottom. This, he said, must mean that the atoll was the summit of a submarine mountain whose sides were steeper than that of the sheerest volcanic cone. Lyell's theory was that the atolls were built on submarine craters. But Darwin doubted this, for many atolls were oblong. Among the Maldiva, one was eighty-eight miles long and between ten and twenty miles wide. No volcano could possibly have such a shape!

Then, too, some were not bounded by narrow reefs but by a vast number of separate little atolls. Others arose out of the great central lagoons. And all the coral islands rose to the same height, just above the water. Where in the world would one find a range of volcanic mountains with even two pinnacles equally high?

He wondered how thick the coral layer was. After experimenting he and Fitzroy tried another experiment and discovered that reef-building corals lived at no greater depth than twenty to thirty fathoms. And it must follow then that wherever there was an atoll, some foundation must have originally existed below the surface.

But what was this foundation? It could not have been

built from sediment. Surely no river could have carried deposits to pile up a mountain in the middle of the ocean to a level of twenty fathoms from the surface. He had already set aside the possibility of a volcanic "elevatory force" that could have raised mountains of such even-shaped oblongs. There could be only one answer—subsidence.

As mountain after mountain, island after island, slowly sank beneath the water, they provided a fresh base for the growth of corals. As the land continued to sink, the living animals continued building up toward the surface. Since corals died once out of the water, the islands were just higher than sea level, by virtue of coral fragments thrown by the waves on top of the living coral.

"We see in each atoll a monument over an island now lost," was Darwin's conclusion—a conclusion which has only recently been fully confirmed by modern scientists. When in 1946, in preparation for atomic test explosions, borings were made in the Bikini atoll, it was demonstrated that the coral formations—mostly dead—reached down to a depth of 7000 feet. Over untold millions of years, the steady work of these primitive organisms had built up the islands as they steadily sank. In a race with the subsiding land, the animals, reaching for the surface of the water, won out.

In the middle of the summer, Charles wrote to Caroline from the island of Ascension: "How beautiful Shropshire will look, if we can but cross the wide Atlantic, before the end of October . . . And as for your boundless plains and impenetrable forests, who could compare them with the green fields & oak woods of England? . . ."

12

A Naturalist's Cargo

SUNDAY, October 2, 1836—Sailing into a stormy Channel, in drenching rain and a southwest gale, the brig dropped anchor in Falmouth Harbor, at the southwest tip of England.

Darwin came ashore with but one thought—a coach to take him home to Shrewsbury. He was weak from days of severe seasickness; the driving rain reminded him of the miserable weeks before his departure from Plymouth. He was glad to be on the night mail coach eastward.

The next day, as the coach climbed the western hills, he was still tired and impatient. By Tuesday morning, he was recovering and his spirits rose. Looking out over the English countryside, he was deeply moved by the beauty of his homeland. The fields stretched fresh and green among the woods and orchards in their fall colors. The charming clean villages with their old churches and thatched cottages, the farm laborers turning over the soil in fall plowing, the rich cultivated land, the rolling hills—this was home. How could the dozing passengers be so indifferent to the gentle beauty of the scene?

He reached Shrewsbury at midnight on Tuesday and went to the Lion Inn, so as not to disturb his family. The next morning before breakfast, he hurried to the Mount and walked into the house unannounced. What excitement in the Darwin household!

His sisters, his father, and the servants rushed to greet him with happy rejoicing. His father declared that the shape of his head had changed and his sisters noticed that he was a little thinner. The gardeners and stablemen celebrated the occasion by getting drunk. Only his dog took his homecoming calmly and greeted Charles as if he had never been away.

Charles was deliriously happy to be home, to find his family well, to catch up on all the bits of family news that letters omitted, and to learn how Erasmus was getting along. He had endless questions about the family at Maer and immediately dashed off a note to Uncle Jos. "I am so very happy I hardly know what I am writing," he said. He hoped to see them all soon, especially to thank his "first Lord of the Admiralty" for making the voyage possible. Uncle Jos had been absolutely right about this rare opportunity of seeing men and things, and Charles was deeply grateful.

Concluding his diary during the first few days at home, he balanced the "pains & pleasures" of global wanderings. Were he asked to advise anyone on such an undertaking, he would say that it should be considered only with a serious purpose in mind. The wonders of seeing many countries and people must be weighed against the evils—the loss of companionship, separation from family and friends, the lack of space, privacy and rest, and the comforts of civilization. And finally, there were the miseries of seasickness.

But he could not fail to treasure his experiences: the

grand, virgin forests, the views from lofty mountains, the volcanoes in action, the white peak of Teneriffe, water-spouts, lovely coral islands, primitive man in desolate Tierra del Fuego, the fossils at Punta Alta revealing the secrets of past ages, the constellations of the southern hemisphere. Even the vast, sterile wastes of Patagonia had their fascination. "In conclusion—it appears to me that nothing can be more improving to a young naturalist, than a journey in distant countries . . . I have too deeply enjoyed the voyage not to recommend to any naturalist to take all chances. . . ."

What next? What became of his intention of entering the Church? For a time, he and his father had assumed that the voyage would merely postpone his taking holy orders. But now it was clear that Charles would travel along a very different path. The idea of his becoming a clergyman had died a natural death.

Toward the end of the voyage, his sisters had written Charles of Professor Sedgwick's prediction that he would take his place among the leading scientists. The collection of fossils sent to Henslow had created a stir. Henslow, before Darwin's return, had read some of his letters before the Philosophical Society of Cambridge; in fact, had had them printed for distribution to its members. This news from home had so elated Darwin's spirits that, as he wrote Henslow, "I clambered over the mountains of Ascension with a bounding step, and made the volcanic rock resound under my geological hammer."

After a few days' rest, and even before visiting Maer, Charles wrote to Henslow. Now that he was home, what was he to do about putting his specimens in order? He hurried off to Cambridge to consult with his old professor and then went to Greenwich to bring his treasured cargo ashore. He went on to London where Lyell was eager to talk with him. Darwin was extremely anxious to meet the famous geologist, to tell him how deeply his book had influenced his own development as a scientist. He also needed Lyell's advice on what to do about his enormous collection.

There were others in London who had followed Darwin's trail blazing travels and were on hand to welcome him. He stayed with Erasmus in his rooms at 43 Great Marlborough Street, where he was welcomed by old friends and his cousin Hensleigh Wedgwood, now married to Frances Mackintosh. Men of science greeted young Darwin with excited interest. He dined at the Linnean and Geological Societies and was elected a Fellow of the Geological and Zoological Societies.

For months he had been looking forward to meeting his idol, Lyell. Face to face with the handsome, affable, and eager-minded scientist, Darwin was charmed. He came as a disciple, but Lyell listened to him as a peer in a common scientific pursuit. Most particularly, the older man was eager to talk about Darwin's theory of coral formations. When Darwin explained his idea, Lyell jumped up excitedly— Lyell was obviously impressed. Prancing about the room and chuckling with delight, he marvelled at the utter simplicity of Darwin's explanation. He did not in the least mind that it demolished his own theory of volcanic craters. In fact, he declared that the distribution of coral reefs could serve as a guide to mapping out areas of subsidence and elevation!

Lyell urged Darwin to prepare a paper on the subject to be presented to the Geological Society. Darwin basked in this warm approval and encouragement from the man he considered his master. It was like Lyell, he said, to show "hearty sympathy with the work of other scientific men." The friendship begun in this generous sharing of enthusiasm became important to both men.

Housing Darwin's collections was a problem. There was as yet no natural history museum; the Zoological Society museum was too small. Besides, some zoologists failed to recognize the value of his finds. There seemed to be no room for his collections in London and Henslow and Lyell both urged Charles to assemble and put them in order at Cambridge. So he had all his specimens sent there and planned to spend the winter working over them. Meanwhile, he finished up his London errands and at last was free for visits to the Mount and Maer.

Caroline, bursting with pride in the brother who had left England a nobody and had returned to find himself a young scientist of note, went with him to Maer. She had prepared him for the great change in dear Aunt Elizabeth, who was failing in body and mind. And Cousin Fanny had died during his absence. Fanny and Emma, the babies of the family, had been known as the Dovelies or, on occasion, as Mustard and Pepper. It was strange to see Emma without her inseparable companion in sweet mischief; Emma the popular belle giving up parties and balls to devote herself to her mother.

But Uncle Jos, with three sons and two daughters still living at home, made Maer, as always, the warmest household Charles had ever known. The entire family, with friends and neighbors, welcomed him back and bombarded him with questions about his adventures all around the globe. After the first hours of excited talk had simmered down, there was a Wedgwood-Darwin council on Charles' immediate plans.

There was the problem of the publication of his *Beagle* diary. Toward the end of the voyage, Fitzroy had asked to see parts of it. He liked it well enough to suggest that portions be included in his own account of the voyage. Charles hadn't considered his day to day notes worthy of publication but he agreed to the Captain's proposal.

His family, however, had read the sections he sent home and they insisted that he publish his material separately.

Caroline was especially insistent and Uncle Jos and cousin Emma also urged independent publication. And so it was settled, after Fitzroy gave his consent.

In December, Charles returned to Cambridge. After a few days' stay at the Henslows', he settled in his own lodgings for the work on his collection would require several months. It was a vast undertaking and, except for Henslow, he received all too little help. Often discouraged, he would ask himself if all the laborious gathering of fossils had been a waste of time. If he hadn't been on "a King's ship," he would have been tempted to turn his collections over to the French museums. But eventually his amazing global harvest was distributed to good advantage in the British Isles.

Richard Owen of the College of Surgeons, who was writing a history of extinct mammals, was eager for the fossils of four new genera in Darwin's collection (only two extinct South American genera had been known previously). Dr. Grant, Charles' Edinburgh friend, was interested in the corals. There were still birds, reptiles, insects and a variety of marine animals, and extinct species dug out of silt and clay to be arranged, classified, and housed. Due to Darwin's persistent efforts, all these finally got into safe hands.

He was happy to be back in Cambridge, though he missed his schoolmates. But there were still Henslow, Sedgwick, and others of the older men with whom he dined and spent the evenings sociably. Often he stayed home to work over his diary, for his days were devoted to his specimens. He interrupted this schedule in January to read a paper before the Geological Society in London on "Proofs of Recent Elevation of the Coast of Chili." He was formally installed as a Fellow of the Society and a month later became a member of its Council.

By March, his Cambridge work was finished and he had to spend the next months in "dirty, odious London." Even in the five years of his absence it had gotten dirtier, noisier, and more crowded than ever.

The railway, at first regarded as a newfangled means of carrying freight, was now taking passengers. It was faster and cheaper than stagecoach travel and daring souls were now boarding the new railroad carriages. Emma Wedgwood and Catherine Darwin, on their first railway trip about this time, were so impressed with the speed of barely ten miles an hour that they urged their relatives to try this new sensation.

Thousands of miles of track, radiating from London, were being laid in a fever of building. The railway boom created a demand for labor and there was a steady migration from the villages into the factories of large cities, London included. The continued growth of industry meant more workers' homes, grime, dirt, bustle, and noise.

Charles took rooms close to Erasmus. His brother, never in robust health, had long since given up any idea of practicing medicine. He enjoyed his leisurely life as a patron of the arts and letters. In his elegant home with its fine library, he entertained distinguished friends and his gentle charm made him a cherished figure among the intellectual elite. It was through Erasmus that Charles met Thomas Carlyle and Thomas Macaulay. He admired Macaulay's knowledge of history and shared his liberal views on Parliamentary reform. But at Erasmus' dinner parties, he found Carlyle overbearing, talkative and Jenny Carlyle's hysterical giggle irritating.

He enjoyed much more the quiet dinners with the Lyells and with Richard Owen, and his renewed acquaintance with Leonard Horner whom he had known in Edinburgh.

Darwin was rapidly becoming at home in scientific circles. He read a paper on the South American ostrich before the Zoological Society and was active in the discussions of the

Geological Society. These stimulating contacts with men of science and the intimate companionship of Hensleigh and Frances Wedgwood, and visits from his sisters made London bearable.

It was now decided that once his *Journal* was completed, Charles should publish his zoological materials of the voyage. This was an immense job, requiring the help of competent zoologists. Besides, there was the financing of such a book. Could the British Treasury be persuaded to foot the bill if Darwin undertook the work?

With considerable hesitancy, Darwin requested a grant from the Chancellor of the Exchequer and was pleasantly surprised when a thousand pounds was cheerfully granted. Writing to Henslow, Charles said: "I expected a rather awful interview, but I never found anything less so in my life. It will be my fault if I do not make a good work."

By the summer, the *Journal* was near completion and in August, the first proof sheets were sent in. He was working hard. Encouraged by Lyell, he wrote papers for the Geological Society on the fossil deposits of Punta Alta and on the areas of elevation and subsidence in the Pacific and Indian Oceans. He was asked to serve as honorary Secretary of the Society and took on this added service for three years.

He felt the strain of life in London and was troubled with palpitations, as he had been before the voyage. A much needed rest came in Shrewsbury and at Maer, where the families were celebrating Caroline's engagement to cousin Josiah. They had all waited years for this happy event. Now that it was decided, the wedding took place promptly, a few weeks later.

In November, the first printed copy of the *Journal* came off the press. Formal publication was delayed until 1839, when Fitzroy's two volumes came out, but meanwhile copies were circulated among his friends. Darwin felt the thrill and pride of a new author. Years later, he wrote: "The success of this my first literary child always tickles my vanity more than that of any of my other books." He told Henslow that if he lived to be eighty, he would not cease to marvel at finding himself an author.

The next task was to map out his zoology book. It was planned that Professor Owen would write the account of the fossil mammals, George Waterhouse of the recent mammals, Henslow's brother-in-law, the Reverend John L. Jenyns of the fish, John Gould of the birds, and Thomas Bell of the reptiles. Darwin was to edit the whole and contribute introductory sections on the habits and range of each species. This proved to be a long and tedious work, the last section not finished until 1842. When it finally appeared in five large quarto volumes splendidly illustrated with color plates, Darwin's zoological studies impressed the whole scientific world.

While this laborious task was weighing heavily on his shoulders, Darwin was impatient to get on with the baffling and, for him, the most absorbing subject—the evolution of species. He was working out explanations for the extinction of certain species, the rise of others, the capacity of some and the failure of others to adapt to changing conditions. In July, 1837, the moment his *Journal* was finished, he wrote the first outline of his problem and for the next twenty years he filled notebook after notebook with his observations and reflections. He told nobody of his great preoccupation, not even Lyell, his closest scientist-friend.

In June, 1838, Emma Wedgwood and sister Catherine stopped off in London on their way home from a visit to Paris. It was the year of the coronation of Queen Victoria, who was to reign over the expanding empire until just after the turn of the century.

Francis Galton, grandson of Erasmus Darwin by his

second marriage, also came to London for the coronation and stayed with his cousin Charles. The two had much in common. Galton had made some geographical studies of Africa and in later years was to discover color blindness and make important studies of heredity. While Galton paid thirty shillings for a seat to see the elaborate procession, Charles was satisfied to watch it from a friend's window. He would have had a closer feeling toward his young queen if he had known how she ended that solemn day. She ran up the palace stairs, took off her stiff finery, and gave her dog, Dash, an evening bath.

Catherine and Emma had rooms next door and Charles saw much of them during their visit. He was beginning to realize that he had more than a cousin's affection for Emma. Approaching thirty, he was weighing the advantages and disadvantages of married life. He scribbled down the equation. On the plus side there were children, constant companionship, the charms of music, and female chitchat. On the other hand, it meant a terrible loss of time, a struggle against too much social life, and the expense of a possibly large family.

In the end, however, he concluded: "My God, it is intolerable to think of spending one's whole life like a neuter bee, working, working, and nothing after all . . . Imagine living all one's days solitarily in smoky, dirty London house—only picture to yourself a nice soft wife on a sofa, with good fire and books and music perhaps—compare this vision with the dingy reality of Gt. Marlboro' St. Marry, marry, marry. Q.E.D."

In the eyes of any young woman, Charles would have been considered attractive. With his unusual height of six feet and his serious face with deepset grey eyes, he was striking. Emma, who had known him all her life, treasured his lovable qualities—his warm, unpretentious gentleness, his open honesty, good-humored and boyish enthusiasm. She had a shrewd insight into people and found Charles the first young man she had met who fascinated her. She was frankly bored with much that others considered above criticism—Shakespeare's plays, for instance—but she had an intuition of greatness in Charles.

When his visitors had gone, Charles was off to Scotland on a geological trip and a visit to Edinburgh. In the fall, he left for a brief holiday at Maer determined to ask Emma for her hand. But he was afraid she might refuse him and left without proposing. Back in London, he was forced to cut down work on his book on coral reefs and volcanoes. He had been driving himself too hard and was exhausted. Emma was very much on his mind. Quite suddenly, he decided one day in November to go to Shrewsbury and then with Catherine went on to Maer. When he asked Emma to marry him, she gave her consent without the least hesitation. She had long hoped that Charles would propose and had nearly given him up.

Dazed with happiness, Emma tried to teach her Sunday School class as usual but gave up the attempt and rushed home. Charles, too, was overwhelmed. He looked perfectly miserable and had a wretched headache. One would have thought him a rejected suitor. That evening when the usual houseful of guests had gone, the lovesick pair broke the news to the Wedgwoods, who sat up half the night celebrating. The next day, Charles and Catherine carried the glad tidings to Shrewsbury.

Dr. Darwin was as delighted as Uncle Jos and between them they arranged a handsome income for the young couple. Uncle Jos promised a wedding gift of 5000 pounds and a yearly allowance of 400. To Robert he wrote: "I could have parted with Emma to no one for whom I would so soon and so entirely feel as a father, and I am happy in believing that Charles entertains the kindest feelings for his uncle father."

It is rare enough that a love match coincides so completely with family hopes. Emma wrote her Aunt Jessie Sismondi, whom the Wedgwood girls often visited in Switzerland: "It is a match that every soul has been making for us, so we could not have helped it if we had not liked it ourselves." Knowing her Charles, she set down the qualities she loved in him: "He is the most open, transparent man I ever saw, and every word expresses his real thoughts. He is particularly affectionate and very nice to his father and sisters, and perfectly sweet tempered."

Aunt Jessie was not surprised at the news, for long ago she had read Emma's palm and known she would marry a Darwin. But, she wrote Emma, "seeing Charles did not come on, I began to fear it was Erasmus." (Poor Erasmus was considered eccentric by most of the family.) She went on to give her niece a bit of advice about her one failing: carelessness in dress. Emma's nickname as a girl had been Miss Slip-Slop because she had no notion of order and, in this elaborately-dressed age, she had no interest in the intricacies of fashion.

"If you do pay a little more," Aunt Jessica urged, "be always dressed in good taste; do not despise those little cares which give everyone more pleasing looks, because you know you have married a man who is above caring for such little things. No man is above caring for them."

Emma would cheerfully have turned herself into a fashion plate to please Charles but they were never to be bothered by little things because they shared such great things: selfless devotion, love of freedom and tranquility, and a wonderful gift for radiating that special Wedgwood-Darwin quality of loving understanding. Charles had already developed that gift, in spite of the oppressive atmosphere of the Mount. As for Emma, she was a genius at making those close to her feel cherished and comforted.

She had grown up in that atmosphere, the family pet of a household where the windows and doors were always open and the children were never punished, but were kept too busy and happy to need more than the gentlest correction. Josiah's rules for bringing up small children were based on Rousseau and they worked very well with Emma. She might be Miss Slip-Slop about keeping her room in order but she grew up with a firm, strong character. Her great gift was the piano. She had lessons from Chopin and when George IV's Mrs. Fitz Herbert visited Emma's London boarding school, Emma was chosen to play for the visitor. To the end of her life, she played a little every day for her own pleasure.

Emma went through the rounds of a fashionable young lady—trips to London and Europe, concerts, theaters, balls, proposals of marriage from young men who failed to interest her. She got more satisfaction from her Sunday School for sixty poor children, held in the laundry at Maer. This was really a school, the only one these children had. She taught them their letters and wrote little stories, which she had printed in large type. Later, she was to teach her own children to read from these same primers.

Emma was a few months older than Charles, in her thirtieth year. She was the right height, reaching to his shoulder, she was well-built and graceful, she had lovely hands and a face expressing her dignity and charm: serene grey eyes, sweet mouth, and calm brow under smoothly parted chestnut hair drawn into clusters of curls over her ears.

Fortunately, Emma understood nothing of science. When she told Charles that she was going to try to read Lyell's

Principles of Geology, he warned her off in great alarm. "Depend upon it, you will hereafter have plenty of geology," he assured her.

Back in London, Charles was showered with congratulations from relatives and friends who agreed that he had undoubtedly "drawn a prize." He now set about finding a home, which for the next few years must be in London. Emma would have liked a house in the country but London was necessary for his work.

After much search, he and Erasmus found a house at 12 Upper Gower Street that would have to do. Its one redeeming feature was a small, rear garden which offered some quiet. The interior and furnishings were so garish that he nicknamed it "Macaw Cottage." In January, Charles moved in with his mass of geological specimens. His old cabin boy, Covington, was pressed into service as man-servant and the London Wedgwoods helped make the place livable.

During the preparations, on a visit to Maer, Charles had misgivings about Emma's happiness. From this beautiful, gay household, he was taking her to the solitude of a London house to share the life of a man who was ever lost in his thoughts and scientific pursuits. Would she be content with the simple, quiet life he had grown accustomed to? Emma knew her mind and never once swerved where Charles was concerned.

On January 29, 1839, Charles and Emma were married in a simple ceremony at Maer Church. That same day they departed for their London home, where they found the fires blazing and the house looking comfortable and inviting.

Married life was all he had hoped for but obligations were a strain. There was the first at-home and the first dinner party for Erasmus and the Hensleigh Wedgwoods. Professor Sedgwick came to visit and later, the Henslows spent a few days with them. The Lyells and Mrs. Lyell's sister were frequent visitors. Sir John Herschel, whom Charles had met at Capetown, made a call. They were often invited out; they went to the theater, a passion of Emma's.

Modest as these social evenings were, they proved too much for Charles, who invariably awoke with a headache and nausea the next day. By the end of the year, he was quite ill. In the fall, they spent a few idle weeks in Shrewsbury and Maer and on their return settled down to await their first child.

On December 27, 1839, which happened to be the eighth anniversary of the *Beagle's* sailing, William Erasmus Darwin was born. There never was a father more proud and delighted with his charming baby than Darwin. He called the blue-eyed boy Mr. Hoddy-Doddy or Doddy for short.

The *Journal and Remarks*, completed two years before, came out that summer as the third volume of four describing the two *Beagle* expeditions. It had already been enthusiastically read in final page form by Henslow, Lyell, and Owen. A young botanist, Joseph Hooker, had slept with it under his pillow, so that he could get to it immediately on awaking. This young admirer of Darwin became the most steadfast of his scientific friends. Now that his book reached the public, it was warmly received and by the end of the year was reissued as a separate book instead of part of a series. A third edition was out in 1840. *The Voyage of the Beagle,* as it is called, turned out to be one of the most delightful travel books ever written.

Charles' continued illness prevented him from doing sustained work on his book on coral reefs. His long spells of enforced idleness were enlivened by his scientific and fatherly study of Doddy's "expression of the emotions."

Darwin's interest in the origin of animal and human expression became the subject of a later work.

The supervisory work on the volumes dealing with the animal studies of the voyage was very much on his mind. When his health permitted, he worked on *Coral Reefs.* It was a little book, but it "cost twenty months of hard work" because he had to read every work on the subject and consulted many charts on the Pacific Islands. But he was satisfied that his theory of coral island formation was sound. In January, 1842, the manuscript went to the printer.

Darwin's abiding interest in the origin of species, however, took precedence over all else. He continued to collect facts on this subject even when he was too ill to work on other things. Under the heading of *Transmutation of Species* he jotted down every thought, observation, and question that crossed his mind in his diary:

> It is a wonderful fact, horse, elephant, and mastodon, dying about the same time in different quarters. Will Mr. Lyell say that same circumstance killed it over a tract from Spain to South America?—(Never.)

Such were the raw materials—his gropings and doubts as well as persistent facts—which began to take on the shape of a cohesive theory. By the middle of 1842, he had the skeleton around which to build his great work during the next fifteen years. In thirty-five pages, he had set down the outline for what was to become *The Origin of Species.* It began with the variations in species of domesticated animals, man's use of variations—the selective breeding of race horses from the fleetest runners, for instance.

In nature, however, what was the force that caused changes in wild species? One day he picked up Thomas Robert Malthus' *Essay on Population.* Malthus declared that human populations, multiplying more rapidly than the available food supply, were kept in check by destructive forces —war, disease, and famine. This idea was of tremendous importance to Darwin. It gave him a clue to his greatest puzzle, how and why species are changed. He never forgot the electric flash of the moment when he discovered what he called "natural selection." He wrote,

> . . . under these circumstances favourable variations would tend to be preserved, and unfavourable ones to be destroyed. The result of this would be the formation of new species. Here then I had at last got a theory by which to work; but I was so anxious to avoid prejudice, that I determined not to for some time write even the briefest sketch of it.

And so the germ of a great idea was stored away until, nurtured on endless facts collected over two decades, it was finally to flower.

The Darwins were increasingly aware that London, with all its demands on Charles' time and energies, was endangering his health. Their second child, Anne Elizabeth, was born in 1841, during the second winter of Darwin's illness, through which Emma nursed him back to health. In 1842, they were expecting their third baby. During that summer, they went house hunting in the country, looking for a suitable place at a moderate price and near enough to London so that Charles could make occasional necessary trips to town.

The house they settled on was in Kent, near the village of Downe and was bought for them by Dr. Darwin for 2200 pounds. On September 14th, nine days before Mary Eleanor was born, they moved to Down House. The first months in the home they were to occupy for the rest of their lives were saddened by the death of the baby after only three weeks.

Down House

ONLY SIXTEEN MILES from London Bridge, Downe was and still is a quiet rural spot in the chalk district of Kent. The village and farms were set on a fertile plateau but the steep, streamless valleys below gave the country a bare look. Yet to Darwin it was full of charm, with its many flowers, lonely woods, and muddy red clay lanes. Its "extreme quietness and rusticity" were especially soothing to him after the confusion of London.

Even years later, when a railway spur was built, there was still a four mile ride from the station to Downe village, through a deep narrow lane where the trees met overhead.

The square, unpretentious Down House of weathered brick stood in about eighteen acres of land, just beyond the village. The Darwins spent the first spring and summer making this bare three-story building into a comfortable home. The brick walls were covered with stucco and the loose slate of the roof repaired. A large bay was added on all three floors, overlooking the garden.

Drawing room, dining room, and study were low-ceilinged and roomy, with sashed windows reaching to the floor. There were plenty of bedrooms on the upper floors for their growing family and guests. Drinking water was drawn by a squeaking pump from a deep well under the nursery window. There was no bathroom and the housemaids carried hot water to the rooms in big brown-painted bath cans for the wash basins and tubs.

The furnishings were "dignified and plain" and according to one grandaughter, "reflected the barer way of life of the early nineteenth century, rather than the crowded, fussy mid-Victorian period." The four-poster beds had canopies and bed curtains but the Darwins avoided the heavy overstuffed chairs and sofas, ornate hangings, massive woods, Oriental rugs, pink and purple beflowered crockery knickknacks, romantic statuary, and heavy cut glass so much admired in their day.

Outdoors, there was the same easy simplicity. The Maer grounds laid out by Capability Brown had taught the Darwins the wisdom of letting nature create her own landscapes. A row of fine lime trees on the west side of the large lawn provided seclusion. The gay flower beds set out under the drawing room windows were in full view from the inside. The house itself before long became covered with creepers and the long pebbled walk to the kitchen was shaded by tall syringa and lilac bushes. Shrubbery and orchards sheltered the house on three sides. The south side faced on an open field bordered at the far end by woodland. Although the sea was forty miles away, on days of strong southwest gales there was brine on the drawing room window panes.

On the lawn were two yew trees where the children had their swings and under a bay tree was heaped a pile of sand for their play. Beyond the row of lime trees stood the orchard and beyond that the kitchen garden, and later

Darwin's greenhouse where he carried on some of his experiments. Then came an acre strip of trees which he himself planted. It was ringed with a sandwalk, a distinctive feature of Down and Darwin's special property.

He loved the country with its walks through quiet woods, the red clay of plowed fields, the wild flowers, the bird notes, and the drone of bees. Here in almost complete seclusion from the noisy, bustling world, he found a haven for observing, experimenting, meditating, and writing.

The first years at Down were shadowed by the baby's death and Uncle Jos' long illness. He died in July of 1843, and Emma and Charles made a sad journey to Maer to say farewell to the best of fathers. Aunt Elizabeth was spared grief, for her mind was completely gone now.

In September, their fourth child Henrietta was born and the Scotch nanny, Brodie, began a long reign over the nursery. The work on the house and garden were completed. The house, so uninviting at first, was transformed into a home where parents and children were to spend years of increasing happiness.

Darwin was again at work on the second part of the geology of his voyage, the *Volcanic Islands*. This was the book he had conceived of writing ten years earlier, daydreaming on the sunny shore of St. Jago. It was completed by 1844, early enough for Darwin to turn to transplanting evergreens, before taking a holiday at Shrewsbury and Maer.

He visited his father at least twice a year, happy to find they were no longer at odds. Dr. Darwin, in fact, was now the kind, generous parent Charles had always felt he was.

Charles' materials on species were accumulating. He subscribed to breeders' journals and read piles of agricultural and horticultural books, to study how plants and animals were changed under domestication. He sought information from his cousin, William Fox, who was then engaged in crossing fowl, ducks, and pigeons. Would Fox send him any material on the results of his breeding experiments?

He corresponded more extensively with Joseph Hooker, the young botanist, whom he had first met in 1839. He was the son of Sir William Hooker, director of the Royal Botanical Gardens at Kew, and botany was his birthright. It was Hooker who had slept with the sheets of the *Journal* under his pillow. He was so fascinated by Darwin's account of the voyage that he determined literally to follow his footsteps. On a four year expedition, he covered much of the ground explored by the *Beagle* and then went on to the Antarctic.

Soon after Hooker's return in 1843, Darwin wrote, begging details of his expedition, which he had followed eagerly in Hooker's letters to Lyell. Hooker was one of the first visitors at Down; thereafter Darwin continued to consult him as an expert botanist. He sent Hooker some of the plants he had collected in Patagonia and urged, "Do make comparative remarks on the species allied to the European species, for the advantage of botanical ignoramuses like myself."

Rapidly taking first place in Darwin's confidence, Hooker was the first to hear about Darwin's ideas on species. "I have been now ever since my return engaged in a very presumptuous work, and I know no one individual who would not say a very foolish one," he confided.

He went on to explain how he was struck with the distribution of the Galapagos plants and animals and with South American fossils. "At last gleams of light have come, and I am almost convinced (quite contrary to the opinion I started with) that species are not (it is like confessing a murder) immutable . . . I have found out (here's presumption!) the simple way by which species become exquisitely adapted to various ends." To Darwin's great delight and astonishment Hooker's study of his Galapagos specimens bore him out.

By the summer of 1844, Darwin had put flesh around his skeleton outline of two years before. In two hundred and thirty pages, he explained his views on the variation in organisms both under domestication and in their natural state and the evidence for and against the view that species "are naturally formed races descended from common stocks." A copy went off to Hooker for his evaluation.

What was the evidence on which Darwin based his firm belief that species could not have been "separately created" by individual acts of the Will of a Creator? There was, for instance, the geographical distribution of related species— the wider the distance that separated them, the more dissimilar they were. Then, the close resemblance between species in each large group or genus; the almost identical embryos of the pig, calf, and rabbit; the vestiges of once useful parts, such as the gills in the tadpole stage of salamanders now living on land. From a mass of concrete evidence, he became convinced that all organisms—extinct and living—descended with modifications from a few forms, perhaps ten or less.

The importance which Darwin attached to this sketch was revealed in a letter to Emma which she would find if he died suddenly.

> If, as I believe, my theory in time be accepted even by one competent judge, it will be a considerable step in science. I therefore write this in case of my sudden death, as my most solemn and last request, which I am sure you will consider the same as if legally entered in my will, that you will devote 400 pounds to its publication, and further, will yourself, or through Hensleigh take the trouble in promoting it.

While the work on species continued, he kept up also with his geological writings. The third and final volume stemming from the *Beagle* experience, *Geological Observations on South America,* was begun in 1844. He found writing exhausting, almost painful, and often wondered whether it was worth the effort to write books which, with his accustomed modesty, he believed would not be read. Yet he went on, finishing this project, like the others he had undertaken. When the three volumes were completed and a new revised edition of the *Journal* appeared in 1845, the story of the voyage was fully told. It had taken ten long, hard years to put into print what Darwin had seen during his circumnavigation of the globe.

But for the extraordinary calm, evenness, and harmony of life at Down, one could hardly account for the volume of work that Darwin produced, invalided as he was for so much of his life. The idyllic existence that struck every visitor in the Darwin household was compounded of many ingredients: Charles' equable nature, Emma's unending devotion and limitless patience in caring for her ailing husband, the joy both derived from loving and gifted children, and from simple, unpretentious living. And they had the good fortune to possess means as generous as their impulses.

The Darwins had ten children, two of whom, Mary Eleanor and Charley Waring, died in infancy. After William and Henrietta came George in 1845, Elizabeth (1847) Francis (1848) Leonard (1850) and Horace in 1851. In that same year, Anne Elizabeth, their second child died at the age of 10, nearly breaking her father's heart.

From the sketch by Francis of his "Father's Everyday Life," we get an intimate glimpse of life in Down.

> No one indeed, except my mother, knows the full amount of suffering he endured, or the full amount of his wonderful patience . . . her days were so planned

that all his resting hours might be shared with her. She shielded him from every avoidable annoyance, and omitted nothing that might save him trouble, or prevent him becoming overtired, or that might alleviate the many discomforts of his ill-health.

In his relationship towards my mother, his tender and sympathetic nature was shown in its most beautiful aspect. In her presence he found his happiness, and through her, his life—which might have been overshadowed by gloom—became one of content and quiet gladness.

Except for occasional visits to London to attend meetings of the scientific societies, trips which he found wearisome, Darwin's life was a methodical routine. Since even the thought of traveling was disturbing, he preferred to have people come to him. The Lyells, the Hookers, and later the Huxleys were frequent guests; Catherine and Susan Darwin came when they could leave Robert, who was aging and needed care. Emma, the easygoing, charming hostess, made them all feel at home. Even Erasmus, who loathed country life, would visit often, playing with the children and working in the garden.

The Darwins did a great deal to help the humble people of Downe but they limited social exchanges to a few friends who happened to live in the neighborhood. Charles needed to conserve his flickering energies for work and occasional contacts with other scientists. As for diversion, Emma and the children provided endless amusement.

In his well-ordered life, Darwin rose early and went for a short walk before breakfast, a habit he kept almost to the end of his life. Francis, as a little boy, liked to accompany him in the red glow of winter sunrise, a recollection to which he attached a "certain honour and glory." In still earlier walks alone on dark mornings, Darwin on his return would thrill the boys with accounts of foxes he had seen.

He would breakfast alone before eight and then work for about two hours, his most productive time. He would dissect under a simple microscope on a board set into one of his study windows. Through sheer patience and persistence, he overcame much of his natural awkwardness at fine manipulation. At nine-thirty or ten, he came into the drawing room for his mail, hoping it would be light. Resting on a sofa, he would have his letters read to him. After an hour's interval, he returned to work until noon. When he was able to do this much, he was satisfied.

Then he was off on another walk, rain or shine, this time with his dog. His last and most famous pet was Polly, a white fox terrier. When her litter inexplicably vanished, she adopted Charles as her "very big puppy," and was forever licking his face and hair clean. The first stop on this midday walk was generally at the greenhouse. There were germinating seeds to observe or a daily check to be made on some experimental plants. He went on to make the circuit of the sandwalk.

The children always remembered the daily ritual of their father rounding the sandwalk. His son, Francis, wrote:

He walked with a swinging action, using a stick heavily shod with iron, which he struck loudly against the ground, . . . producing a rhythmical click which is with all of us a very distinct remembrance. As he returned from the midday walk, often carrying the waterproof or cloak which had proved too hot, one could see that the swinging step was kept up by something of an effort.

Something always came his way on these walks. His children marvelled at how he was sure to discover birds' nests or the less common birds. He seemed to have a special genius to see what no one else saw. There was the time when some baby squirrels ran up his back and legs, to the consternation of their mother who was barking at them from the tree. And once during his noiseless prowling in the woods, he came upon a sleeping fox, who was so astonished that he didn't run off until after he had taken a sharp stare at the intruder.

At one time when he was collecting grasses, his children became interested in the fascinating project. Darwin was fond of recounting the story of one of his little boys bringing a blade of grass that Darwin had missed. Placing it near his plate during dinner, he proudly announced, "I are an extraordinary grassfinder!"

Fine afternoons were often spent with Emma or the children in the garden, sitting on a bench or lying under one of the lime trees, watching the children at play or recovering a stray tennis ball. His love of flowers was, Francis said, a fusion of scientific interest in structure and admiration for beauty. "I seem to remember him gently touching a flower he delighted in; it was the same simple admiration that a child might have." Experimenting with seedlings, he would personalize them: "The little beggars are doing just what I don't want them to." Even earthworms claimed his affection.

During the afternoon, Darwin read the newspapers and tended to his correspondence. He read the papers by himself but liked to have Emma read aloud novels, history, and travel while he lay on the sofa in the drawing room. Often he would drop off to sleep.

Darwin kept up a lively, voluminous correspondence with men of science and went into careful detail about whatever problems occupied his mind at the moment. A frequent correspondent was the great American botanist, Asa Gray. Darwin's letters had a warm, personal, and informal quality. Seated in an armchair before the fire, he would write the longer letters in rough copy, the paper resting on a support-ing board. Then he would dictate them to Emma or, in later life, to Francis, who became his secretary.

He took great pains in answering letters, even foolish or abusive ones from strangers. Though he had a form printed for acknowledging letters from troublesome correspondents, he rarely used it. All were answered with courtesy and even kindness. He made it a rule to thank people who sent him books and was surprised that so few people acknowl-edged his own liberal distribution of books. He was even more surprised when strangers wrote appreciatively of his writings, which he never expected to interest anybody but his friends.

Correspondence and leisurely reading over, he would work again for an hour in the late afternoon. After dinner he invariably excused himself, "saying that he was an old woman who must be allowed to leave with the ladies." Even a half hour in sociability and conversation sometimes tired him to the point of interfering with his sleep or the next day's work.

An almost unbroken habit in the evening was playing a game of backgammon with Emma. For many years, he carefully kept the game score, with a pretence of serious contest between the partners. After the game was over, he again read some scientific work and, as soon as he showed signs of fatigue, some member of the family would again read to him as he lay on the sofa with a lighted cigarette. He enjoyed listening to the novels of Walter Scott and Jane Austen, but found the tragic ending in some of George Eliot's novels disturbing, as if the character were someone dear to him. When Mark Twain's early stories came out, they were great favorites.

Darwin retired at ten but often lay awake for hours, troubled by some problem that arose in his work or dis-tressed by his physical discomfort. Weekdays and Sundays too, he followed this regular routine of alternating work and rest. But sometimes he was too ill to work even in short snatches.

Despite the handicap of lifelong, almost uninterrupted suffering in nerves and body, Darwin never gave way to impatience or ill humor. He was genial and sweet-tempered even under pressure of work, but especially on summer holidays taken with the family he exhibited, Francis said, " a youthfulness of enjoyment that made his companionship delightful . . . To all of us he was the most delightful play-fellow . . ."

Darwin was passionately attached to his children. He respected their liberty, their thoughts, and opinions. They enjoyed the exhilarating freedom from parental domination which Darwin had never had in his own youth. Even when they were small, the children were at all times on terms of comfortable equality with their parents. Darwin was a cherished playmate and one of his sons, who was four at the time, tried to bribe him with sixpence to come and play during working hours. When Darwin found Leonard jumping up and down on the new drawing room sofa, he merely protested gently, "Oh, Lenny, Lenny, that's against all rules!"

"Then I think you'd better go out of the room," Lenny replied politely.

Though his children never remembered their father scolding them, they never dreamed of disobeying him. They were so apologetic about coming into his study to get some necessity like a bit of string, adhesive, or scissors that he had to reassure the young intruder that he didn't mind being interrupted.

Darwin's sympathetic nature and Emma's outgoing warmth made Down a paradise for children and a household where guests loved to come. Even strangers relaxed in this happy house. Professor De Candolle, a famous French

botanist who visited Down said of Darwin, ". . . in his ease
and naturalness there was . . . a total absence of pretence
or affectation. It was this absence of prose, and the natural
and simple way in which he began talking to his guests, so
as to get them on their own lines, which made him so
charming a host to a stranger."

Darwin attributed his orderly habits of work to his years
on the *Beagle,* where there was no room for untidiness. In
his study, he kept everything within reach. Sitting on a low
revolving stool before his dissecting board, he could turn
left for various tools kept in a round table full of radiating
drawers labelled: "best tools," "rough tools," or "specimens"
or turn right to shelves containing odds and ends—pieces
of glass, saucers filled with sand, biscuit boxes for germinating seeds, zinc labels, thread, and whatnot. His tools were
simple and his equipment makeshift. It seems extraordinary
that he used only a simple microscope. An old three foot
rule, the common property of the household, served him for
taking measurements. For following the growth of plants, he
used a seven foot rod.

Darwin once evaluated his own positive qualities as a
scientist: his power to notice things and his care in observing. In this, he considered himself superior to the common run of men. Very little escaped his attention. His
industry in collecting facts was another. Even more important was "my love of natural science [which] has been
steady and ardent," he concluded his self-appraisal.

To these qualities his son added: never letting exceptions
pass unnoticed; his respect for the value of time, which
made him guard against wasting an experiment through
carelessness; his dogged power of sticking to a subject.

Darwin's perseverance is perhaps best illustrated by his
study of barnacles (*Cirripedia*). When he was on the coast
of Chile, he came across a curious form which burrowed,

instead of clinging in the usual way, to mollusk shells. This barnacle was so different from the rest that he had to create a new suborder to catalogue it. To understand the structure of this unique creature, he began to examine and dissect the whole group. Working on this subject for eight years, he published two thick volumes describing all the known living species and two pamphlets on the extinct ones. Darwin was sure that Sir Edward Bulwer-Lytton had him in mind when he described, in one of his novels, a Professor Long who had written two large volumes on limpets.

The barnacle study had become such an accepted occupation at Down, that when one of the children visiting at a neighbor's home failed to find a dissecting board and microscope he asked, "But where does your father do his barnacles?"

In 1846, ten years after Charles was home from his voyage, Elizabeth Wedgwood died. Nobody could mourn her death half as much as they had mourned the shadowing of her brilliant mind, which had made her seem a ghost in the household where she had been the very soul. But her death meant that Maer too was gone. It was sold to strangers, for all the children were now established elsewhere and they knew that none of them could ever bring back the magic of their childhood days. Charles and Emma had created a home much like Maer but it was sad to see the beautiful old place in alien hands.

Charles went often to Shrewsbury, where his father was in wretched health. He had grown so huge that he could scarcely turn over in bed and, as a doctor, he could diagnose his own case as one whose termination was overdue. He was always glad to see Charles, who he had once predicted would disgrace the family and who was now an acknowledged genius and, what was more important, the happiest member of the family. The Doctor must somehow have had a blighting effect on his children.

Only Marianne, who had escaped early, and Charles, who had voyaged around the world, had married young. Caroline had postponed an ideal marriage until she was nearly forty, Catherine married an elderly widower at fifty-three, and Erasmus and Susan had not married at all. There were many things that Robert Darwin, for all his clairvoyance, could not understand. But when he died in 1848, the poor folk of Frankwell wept as the cortege passed, taking their benefactor to a grave beside Susannah on the Severn bank.

On and off for twenty years, Darwin was gathering material on the problem of species. He had planned some day when he had accumulated enough to write up his work in the "big book." Early in 1856, Lyell, who now knew of his great project, urged him to write out his views fully. With some reluctance, because he never felt that he had exhausted the material necessary to support his views, Darwin began to write. By 1858, twenty-one years after he had begun to jot down his notes on species, he had completed half of the book he had planned on the grand scale.

"But my plans were overthrown . . ." Darwin wrote in his autobiography.

14

The Amazing Coincidence

LOOKING BACK TO 1858, Darwin, in his old age, could calmly say that his plans to publish his major work were "overthrown." But to find the significance of this word, we must trace the story of a man who unintentionally jolted Darwin out of his ordered pace.

Alfred Russel Wallace was born on January 8, 1823, in Usk, a beautiful little village in southwestern England where the Severn enters the British Channel. Wallace was poor and had none of Darwin's advantages of a formal education and, in general, none of Darwin's luck. At fourteen, his schooling was over and he was earning his living. For a year, he worked for his brother in the building trade. Then becoming an apprentice to another brother, a land surveyor and architect, he learned the art of surveying and whatever science such work entailed. Roaming the countryside while surveying in Wales and southwestern England, Wallace became interested in geology. Before long he was "bitten by the passion for species and their description."

When his brother could no longer afford to maintain him as an apprentice, Wallace went to work for a watchmaker. His employer went out of business and for a year, Wallace was an English master in a school in Leicester; then he went back to surveying for a while. At loose ends, he was undecided about what he wanted to do. By chance, he met Henry Walter Bates who influenced him in much the same way Henslow had Darwin.

Two years younger than Wallace, Bates had his career cut out for him by his father—he was to become his partner in hosiery manufacture. In 1844, when the two young men met, they found a common interest in collecting. Wallace had a bent for botany and had set up a herbarium. Bates had the greater knowledge of biology and already possessed a fine collection of beetles and butterflies. The friendship that grew up during the next four years between the self-taught naturalists finally determined their careers. In 1848, they planned a voyage of exploration and collecting to the Amazon region in Brazil.

In this unexplored region, the hunting prospects for still unknown species were excellent. They carried Lyell's *Principles* with them and also Darwin's *Journal*. Bates remained in South America for eleven years and, by the time he returned to England, he had discovered over 8,000 species. Before Darwin's great book was published, Wallace was moving in the same direction. He wrote that on the wings of certain butterflies, "Nature writes, as on a tablet, the story of the modification of species." During the expedition, Bates and Wallace developed from amateur collectors into trained and mature naturalists.

When Wallace was on his way home, a fire broke out on the ship. He and the others of the ship's company were stranded in open boats for ten perilous days and nights, until they were picked up about two hundred miles off the coast of Bermuda. In the fall of 1852, Wallace was back in

England. He had lost his precious collection of insects and birds, notes and drawings, which had been stowed away in the hold of the ill-fated ship.

"Almost all the reward of my four years of privation and danger was lost," he wrote. "What I had hitherto sent home had little more than paid my expenses." The records of his observations during these years had gone up in smoke. But Wallace took his irreplaceable loss with fortitude: "I have need of philosophic resignation to bear my fate with patience and equanimity," he wrote.

Wallace got to work classifying the materials that had been sent home previously. He wrote an account of his travels and spent many months studying the specimens at the Linnean Society, the British Museum, and Kew Gardens. His friends of the Zoological and Entomological Societies encouraged him in his efforts. He attended lectures by Thomas Henry Huxley, who inspired him with his brilliance and originality.

With renewed courage, Wallace decided upon a second voyage—this time to the relatively unexplored Malay Archipelago. With the help of Sir Roderic Murchison, President of the Royal Geographical Society, he obtained passage on the gunboat *Frolic* and sailed for Singapore in January, 1854.

For the next eight years Wallace worked in Malaya, covering fourteen thousand miles in over sixty separate excursions and collecting more than 125,000 specimens. Like Darwin, he was struck with the geographical distribution of species and with the peculiar differences between those in Malaya and South America. Even before his voyage to Brazil, he had begun to think about evolution of species. Writing in retrospect about this period, he said, "I was already speculating upon the origin of species, and taking note of everything bearing upon it that came my way."

A year after his arrival in Malaya, his essay, "The Law

which Has Regulated the Introduction of New Species"
was published in the *Annals and Magazine of Natural History*. Reasoning on the basis of Lyell's evolutionary geology
and his own observation of the geographical distribution
of species, he formulated a law: "Every species has come
into existence coincident both in time and space with a pre-
existing closely allied species."

In 1853, a few months after Wallace had returned to England from his South American adventure, he was introduced
to Darwin, whose *Journal* he greatly admired. This meeting
was a brief, casual encounter between the two naturalists.
Neither could foresee how their destinies were to cross five
years later.

By the summer of 1854, Darwin's books on the barnacles
were completed and he began tidying up his papers and
sending the 10,000 borrowed barnacles out of the house.
He was glad to clear the decks for his ever engrossing
subject of species. He had never ceased to collect facts and
make experiments, nor to speculate about their meaning.
Darwin had no respect for empty speculation, yet he felt
it was useless to accumulate observations without trying
to generalize them. He was convinced that science was
compounded of speculation based on objective fact. In his
own work, he never swerved from this firm belief.

Each new question answered by his painstaking experiments led to a new line of analysis, which, in turn, required
more facts to buttress his reasoning. He confided his theory
only to Lyell and Hooker. He was determined not to announce his project to the scientific world until he was sure
his arguments were without flaw. Only when bolstered with
irrefutable facts could an idea so boldly revolutionary receive sympathetic consideration. He rightly foresaw that
the theory of transmutation of species would meet with
resistance, attack, and even abuse. But if he could convince

three men—Lyell, Hooker, and Huxley—they would, he was sure, act as his champions in the inevitable battle ahead.

Writing in 1857 to Asa Gray, Harvard professor and foremost American botanist, he said he had been scolded by an old friend for corrupting Hooker. This friend had warned that he would do more harm with his idea than ten naturalists could do good. "Now when I see such strong feeling in my oldest friends, you need not wonder that I always expect my views to be received with contempt."

When Wallace's essay on new species came to Lyell's attention in early 1856, he sent a copy of it to Darwin, with a note urging him to hurry his own material into print. Early in May, Darwin had a long talk with Lyell in London. They called Hooker into consultation and he joined in urging Darwin to sketch at once a brief abstract of his theory, to be issued as "a *very thin* and little volume." They were concerned over the possibility of Darwin being forestalled. He set to work on the abstracts.

Lyell continued to prod. On November 10, Darwin wrote him:

I am working very steadily at my book; I have found it quite impossible to publish any preliminary essay or sketch; but I am doing my work as completely as my materials allow without waiting to perfect them. This much acceleration I owe to you.

By the next year several chapters were completed, though he kept stopping to confirm his data. He received a letter from Wallace and replied, "By your letter and even still more by your paper in the Annals, a year or more ago, I can plainly see that we have thought much alike and to a certain extent have come to similar conclusions."

He said he agreed with almost every word of Wallace's

paper. He was preparing his own work for publication and found the subject so very large, that he didn't expect to go to press for two years. In the meantime, he hoped to profit by the "large harvest of facts" he was sure Wallace would reap. "I am glad to be backed by your opinion," he added, concerning the descent of domestic animals. This humility was genuine, but it had its ironic side. For Wallace had been much impressed by Darwin's *Journal* and in his essay had even used Darwin's reflections on Galapagos as part of his argument.

In February, 1858, Darwin wrote his cousin, William Fox, that he was working hard, "perhaps too hard," at his book. "It will be very big. . . . I am like Croesus overwhelmed with my riches in facts, and I mean to make my book as perfect as ever I can. I shall not go to press at soonest for a couple of years . . ."

In the meantime Wallace, thousands of miles away, was continuing his searches in Singapore, Sarawak, Celebes, the Moluccas, Java, and Sumatra. Despite untold hardships, discomforts, and periodic attacks of fever, he traveled by land and sea, observing, collecting, and pondering over the meaning of what he saw. Then one night while he was tossing with fever on the island of Ternate in the Molucca Sea, the meaning of his observations suddenly became crystal clear.

He was convinced by then that species originated by a process of modification passed on by natural descent. Just how, was not so clear. By a strange coincidence he, like Darwin years earlier, was struck with a phrase in Malthus' *Essay on Population*. The same phrase that had sparked Darwin's thinking—"positive checks to increase"—suddenly came to Wallace's mind. Malthus attributed the limitation of population growth to accidents, wars, famine, and disease. Could similar factors operate also to limit the population of animals, Wallace asked himself? And, "as animals breed much more rapidly than does mankind, the destruction each year from these causes must be enormous in order to keep down the number of each species . . ." Wallace wrote later.

Why did some species survive while others perished? The answer then suggested itself: those best adapted survived, while the less well adapted perished. "There suddenly flashed upon me the *idea* of survival of the fittest.

"I seemed to see the whole effect of this, that when changes of land and sea, or of climate, or of food-supply, or of enemies occurred . . . it followed that all the changes necessary for the adaptation of the species to the changing conditions would be brought about . . ."

Losing no time, though still confined to bed, he wrote out his ideas in a new essay, "On the Tendency of Varieties to Depart Indefinitely from the Original Type." The manuscript was off on the next post, arriving at Down on the morning of June 18, 1858.

That is what Darwin meant by the charged words, "But my plans were overthrown . . ."

A brief note accompanied Wallace's manuscript, if Darwin found the paper "sufficiently important" would he send it on to Lyell? He had thought highly of Wallace's earlier essay. Darwin read the manuscript that very day and immediately wrote to Charles Lyell.

> He [Wallace] has today sent me the enclosed, and asked me to forward it to you. It seems to me well worth reading. Your words have come true with a vengeance—that I should be forestalled . . . I never saw a more striking coincidence; If Wallace had my MS. sketch written out in 1842, he could not have made a better short abstract!

Even some of the terms were like his own chapter heads!

Although Wallace didn't ask him to see to the publication of his paper, Darwin intended to write at once offering to send it to some journal. This was Darwin's first thought in asking Lyell to return the manuscript to him. Only then did he permit himself to express his crushing disappointment that after twenty years of labor his priority was taken from him. "So all my originality, whatever it may amount to, will be smashed, though my book, if it will ever have any value, will not be deteriorated; as all the labour consists in the application of the theory."

A week later Darwin again unburdened his troubles to Lyell. What did Lyell think he ought to do? After all, there was nothing in Wallace's sketch which he had not written out more fully in his own outline in 1844. Hooker had read the outline and Asa Gray knew of it from their correspondence. Surely this would show that he had taken nothing from Wallace.

He would be glad to publish a statement of a dozen pages or so, giving his general views, but his conscience held him back: "I cannot persuade myself that I can do so honorably . . ." Since he had not intended to publish any sketch, could he now do so with honor, just because Wallace had sent him an outline of his doctrine, he asked Lyell.

"I would far rather burn my whole book, than that he or any other man should think that I had behaved in a paltry spirit," he went on. Did Lyell think, however, that Wallace, by sending him his sketch, had tied his hands?

Darwin was deeply troubled, "worn out with musings," he wrote. Would Lyell forward his letter to Hooker as well as his own answer? He would then have the benefit of advice from his "two best and kindest friends," as to whether to go ahead with publication. He assured Lyell that he would never again trouble him or Hooker on the subject but the next day he felt impelled to write him a postscript.

To be sure, he could establish his priority, but was it fair to take advantage of Wallace's unsolicited communication and thus prevent him from forestalling him? Yet his own rights were in the balance! "It seems hard on me that I should be thus compelled to lose priority of many years' standing, but I cannot feel at all sure that this alters the justice of the case." Again he appealed to Lyell to find some equitable solution—one that would be fair to both Wallace and himself.

As it turned out, Darwin didn't have to make the final decision. During the next few days he was distraught with illness in the family. His daughter Henrietta contracted diphtheria and Charles Waring, his youngest child, died from scarlet fever which was raging in the village. He sent off a hasty note to Hooker saying that he could not "think now on the subject." He was "quite prostrated" and hardly cared about the matter of priority. He would leave everything to his friends to decide.

And so Lyell and Hooker acted—promptly, with wisdom and justice. Hooker requested the Wallace and Darwin papers. Both were sent to Kew Gardens by messenger. Mrs. Hooker made the necessary copies and Lyell prepared a letter which he and Hooker signed. Two days later, on July 1, 1858, the papers of Wallace and Darwin were presented jointly before the meeting of the Linnean Society.

Never, perhaps, was there a more celebrated meeting in scientific history. In absentia, two men with an identical idea expressed their revolutionary view. Wallace was in far off Malaya. Darwin, grieving over the loss of his infant and panic-stricken as illness spread through his family, was, of course, not present. The gathering was so singularly quiet that it hardly suggested what was happening—the announcement to the world of the theory of evolution, a theory that was to shake the foundation of biology and of society itself.

Francis Darwin reported the occasion in these matter-of-fact words:

> Sir Charles Lyell and Sir J. D. Hooker were present, and both, I believe, made a few remarks, chiefly with a view of impressing on those present the necessity of giving the most careful consideration to what they heard. There was, however, no semblance of a discussion.

Hooker's version in his note to Darwin gave a more accurate picture of what happened.

> The interest excited was intense, but the subject was too ominous for the old school to enter the lists, before armouring. After the meeting it was talked over with bated breath: Lyell's approval, and perhaps in a small way mine, as his lieutenant in the affair, rather overawed the Fellows, who would otherwise have flown out against the doctrine.

Darwin was relieved that the matter had been settled so wisely and honorably. Thanking his friends for their generosity, he wrote to Hooker, "I fancied that I had a grand enough soul not to care, but I found myself mistaken and punished." He felt ashamed, he said, that they had lost time "on a mere point of priority." However, for other reasons, he was gratified that England's renowned geologist and botanist had been his advocates.

Wallace, too, had reason to be satisfied. Until then he had been known only to a few specialists. By the accident of joint publication, he achieved the status of co-discoverer. His esteem for Darwin, the man was now as great as his admiration of Darwin, the scientist. Writing to his mother of the affair, he said, "This assures me the acquaintance and assistance of these eminent men when I return home."

Years later, when the famous meeting was commemorated and Wallace was awarded the first Darwin Medal, he graciously recounted the facts, to avoid future errors as to priority. In his acceptance speech, he estimated his own share as being "roughly, proportional to the time we had each bestowed upon it . . . as twenty years is to one week."

With equal magnanimity, Darwin acknowledged Wallace's contribution. "I cared very little whether men attributed most originality to me or Wallace; and his essay no doubt aided in the reception of the theory," he wrote.

The priority question having been settled with dignity, the two principals returned each to his labors. They had given their views to the world but the world had not yet felt their impact.

15

Masterpiece

THE QUIET RECEPTION of the Darwin-Wallace papers by the Fellows of the Linnean Society was one of physical shock. Like Concepción during the earthquake, every familiar landmark had toppled from its foundations and a tidal wave had carried the debris of old and cherished structures out to sea. There was an interesting reaction that evening. The famous botanist, George Bentham, who was scheduled to read a paper on the fixity of species, heard out the two papers demolishing that idea—and withdrew his own. He had felt the solid ground shift under his feet.

In order to balance Wallace's paper, Darwin in frantic haste had sent his friends part of his 1839 notes on the variation of species and natural selection and a letter written to Asa Gray in 1857 repeating some of these views. They were merely part of Darwin's conception of natural history and formed only two chapters of the great book he published the next year.

But the Darwin-Wallace theory struck at the very heart

of established belief that each kind of plant and animal had been created in its present form, remaining unchanged and unchangeable. Species were *not* fixed for all time, Darwin and Wallace insisted, but developed slowly and gradually and those with the most useful variations survived.

How do these variations, which finally become species, arise? In the struggle for existence. Here Darwin and Wallace invoked Malthus to show why all living beings, besides having to fight such conditions of nature as droughts, must compete for food and living space. For they tend to multiply in geometric ratio; a plant producing only two seeds would in twenty years be the ancestor of a million plants; even the slow breeding elephant would in a few centuries find the planet too small for the descendants of one pair. But this does not happen because each species is kept down by checks: scarcity of food, natural enemies, weather. About as many are destroyed before they can propagate as are born. Thus, the proportion of frogs, bees, sparrows, rabbits, wildcats, hawks, and so on remains about constant in any given area.

It must be so, Darwin argued, because the amount of food for each species must on the average be constant. Thus there is continual competition between members of a species for the available food. What determines which members will live to reproduce? The answer is "some slight variation, profitable to some part of their economy."

The grasshopper with a slight difference in color might be the better disguised from its enemy, the flower a shade brighter than its neighbors would attract the bee and become fertilized. The antelope with shorter or weaker legs would become prey to the wildcat, the fleetest dog would catch the most hares in a time of dearth and survive to pass on his superior qualities to his young. Minute differences in individuals must work to the advantage of one and the disadvantage of others and the best adapted survive.

Or let some change take place in the physical environment or conditions of life, such as a drought or an invasion by locusts or weeds. Existence will then become more difficult for some species, perhaps exterminating them, while others, better adapted, will thrive. Darwin cited the drought in the region of the Plata River. While millions of cattle perished, the whole country swarmed with mice. In that same region, the prickly artichoke, newly introduced from Spain, overran hundreds of miles, killing off the native grass.

In the struggle for existence, the complex relations between animals and plants play a fascinating role. One of the instances Darwin gives in his expanded discussion concerns red clover, which depends absolutely on humblebees for fertilization. No other bees visit the clover, since they cannot reach the nectar. The number of humblebees depends on the number of field mice in the neighborhood, since the mice destroy their combs and nests. But cats destroy mice, so near villages and towns there are plenty of humblebees and the red clover flourishes.

Thus, by an intricate system of checks and balances, living creatures are kept going and kept within bounds. But there is another force at work—natural selection. In his letter to Asa Gray, Darwin spoke of "an unerring power . . . which selects exclusively for the good of each organic being." He believed that nature was working toward perfection, using those slight variations which made the plant or animal better adapted to the conditions under which it lived. How those variations were produced he did not know, for the science of genetics was not yet born. But he believed that variations came through unknown hereditary factors within the organism and that the useful ones tipped the balance for survival. Without using the word evolution, both Darwin and Wallace showed how it worked to create, destroy, or improve species.

All these years, Darwin had been accumulating one section after the other of his vast panorama of life. He wanted to put it all into what he called "the big book," but he was always finding some new detail or some larger vista to enrich his picture. Before he drew the picture which existed in his mind and in his growing piles of notes, he felt compelled to learn more, to check and recheck his facts, to get bits of information from naturalists in distant parts of the globe. What he wanted his "big book" to be was utterly impossible: nothing less than a four-dimensional picture of the world in its immensity, its dizzying antiquity, and its minute, exquisite details; a true and beautiful picture of the world we live in and how it evolved. It could not possibly be done. Now, approaching his fiftieth birthday and racked with aching head and stomach, Charles Darwin did what was possible. He completed the first of a whole series of books which, taken together, suggested the "big book" he could not possibly write.

The shock of Wallace's duplicating part of his own thinking had a salutary effect. He wrote what he called an abstract of his thinking about evolution and this book, turned out in agonizing haste, proved to be the most important book of the nineteenth century. Its shortened title is *The Origin of Species*.

The Darwins were on the Isle of Wight, relaxing after the siege of illness, when Charles began work July 20 on his "abstract." Eight months later, he completed a manuscript that would run to five hundred printed pages. Though the first ten chapters had been drafted before he had received the fateful letter from Wallace, this was tremendously fast work.

Lyell, who was all for getting his friend safely into print before some new calamity occurred, persuaded his own publisher, John Murray, to accept Darwin's book sight unseen. By mid-May, 1859, Murray had read the whole manuscript and regretted his rashness. He was an amateur geologist and a great admirer of Lyell's, but Darwin was going too far. His theory, Murray declared, was absurd. But he had a suggestion. Why shouldn't Darwin write a little book about his observations of pigeons and leave the dangerous theorizing to a later volume? "Everybody is interested in pigeons," he said.

Darwin absolutely refused to change his book and he won out in this tussle with Murray. Safely home at Down, he collapsed and had to go for a water cure at Moor Park, a place in Surrey where he had found help for his nerves on other occasions. He returned to find his proofs waiting, groaned to find his style "incredibly bad," made endless corrections, driven by "an insanely strong wish to finish my accursed book." More water cure and by the end of September the revised proofs were read. He was free of "my abominable volume, which has cost me so much labour that I almost hate it."

A few days later, he left for another watering place in Yorkshire, where the family joined him to stay until early December. By that time he had received surprising news from his publisher. The *Origin of Species* came out on November 24, in a printing of 1250 copies, though Murray had considered five hundred more than enough. It was completely sold out on the day of publication and Murray must have corrections for a second printing at once, if Mr. Darwin please.

One has only to browse in the *Origin* to understand why it went rapidly through six editions. It has the charm of seeing the world of nature through Darwin's incompara-

ble eyes. Like *The Voyage of the Beagle,* this book allows
Darwin to share his delight in the wonders he finds around
him, his intimacy with moth or slug or pigeon suddenly revealing them as the wondrous creatures they, in fact, are.
To the scientists of his own day, most of them with minds
swaddled in suffocating, crippling dogmas, Darwin seemed
either a wicked, blasphemous liar or a liberator. A very
few, like Henslow, took a middle position.

Darwin was intent on telling the truth as he saw it and
he was too much the scientist to quibble. He was not a
zealot, huffing and puffing to get everybody to agree with
him. But he was in a most singular situation, with only
Isaac Newton of his own countrymen, to bear him company. Like Newton, he had discovered a fundamental law,
something that is true for everybody, whether or not they
believe it. This is very different from arriving at a theory.
Darwin had certain theories, some right, some wrong—but
he discovered evolution, a fact as basic as gravity, explaining life as Newton had the physical universe.

With this terrifying knowledge that he had found a universal, undeniable truth, Darwin was staggered by the task
of explaining this truth to his fellow men. He was quite
alone in his conviction. Hooker, Lyell, Asa Gray, even
Wallace, had come only part way with him by the time
he was writing his book. He had worked and pondered
quite alone and now he was opening up his secret to the
world. He knew very well that it would cause shocked
protests, but Newton too had been accused of "introduc-
ing occult qualities and miracles into philosophy." Now
everybody took gravitation for granted. Toward the end
of his book, *The Origin of the Species,* Darwin tried to
forestall such criticism.

> I see no good reason, he wrote, why the views given
> in this volume should shock the religious feelings of

anyone. It is satisfactory, as showing how transient such impressions are, to remember that the greatest discovery ever made by man, namely the law of the attraction of gravity, was also attacked by Leibnitz, "as subversive of natural, and inferentially of revealed, religion."

However, Darwin knew very well what a storm his book would raise and he was cautious and skilful in presenting his case. He began in a disarming way by describing variations in the domestic animals, like horses and pigeons which are deliberately produced by the breeder.

This was familiar ground to the reader and there was nothing too alarming in the next chapter, on variation under nature. Then he lit the fuse of his dynamite, with the sections on the struggle for existence and natural selection and the laws of variation, which he had discovered.

"This whole volume is one long argument," Darwin cheerfully admitted in his last chapter. He devoted five chapters to dealing with the objections people were sure to raise to his theory, not so much arguing, as describing and explaining such matters as how transitions occur, how a simple organ may develop into a highly developed being or into an organ of extreme perfection, like the eye. He discussed instinct, hybridism, and then led into a stunning discussion of "the imperfection of the geological record."

One of the great objections which opponents would raise about the evolution of simple plants or animals into elaborate types was the lack of transitional types or "missing links." First he proves that fossils have, in some cases, filled in the gaps between extinct and living forms. Then he shows how rare and haphazard such discoveries are, describing the complications in the laying down of fossils, so that it is a wonder that any are preserved. "The crust of the earth with its embedded remains must not be looked at as a well-filled museum, but as a poor collection made at hazard and at rare intervals," he said.

Poor as this collection is, Darwin is able to trace living creatures down through the geological ages and to describe their distribution over the globe. With a timetable of millions of years, with very slow and gradual changes, life evolves toward perfection. Now he is ready to come out with bold statements, "I believe that animals are descended from at most only four or five progenitors, and plants from an equal or lesser number." Remembering Asa Gray's algae that were both plant and animal, Darwin admitted that he was sometimes tempted to go further and think that "all animals and plants are descended from some one prototype."

He did not insist on that but he did insist that this long story was a noble one. "There is grandeur in this view of life," he said in his final sentence, ". . . that whilst this planet has gone cycling on according to the fixed law of gravity, from so simple a beginning endless forms most beautiful and most wonderful have been, and are being evolved."

Darwin was on tenterhooks to know how his book would be received. The judges who mattered most—Lyell, Hooker, Huxley, Gray—were quick to reassure him. With a few reservations on certain points, they were convinced. Lyell and Hooker, who had followed the development of his ideas most closely, were astonished at the range and boldness of the *Origin*. The brilliant Huxley exclaimed, "How extremely stupid not to have thought of that!" Asa Gray, a man of great influence among American scientists, became the champion of Darwinism in the United States. In this day of no copyright laws, two American publishers rushed the *Origin* into print and Gray forced one house to withdraw and the other to promise royalties to the author. A

German translation was soon out, unfortunately so poor that at the moment it made little stir.

Erasmus declared his brother's book the most interesting he had ever read. The family, now back at Down House, were elated at the letters which kept pouring in, one of the first from Hooker, who was still reading the "glorious book . . . capitally written. . . . Lyell, with whom we are staying, is perfectly enchanted, and is absolutely gloating over it." Herbert Spencer, himself an ardent evolutionist, declared that he had much to learn from Darwin. One of his reviewers, H. C. Watson, wrote a personal letter declaring "you are the greatest revolutionist in natural history of this century, if not of all centuries."

A letter from Canon Charles Kingsley made Darwin especially happy. For Kingsley, the Queen's chaplain, wrote that he had gradually learned "that it is just as noble a conception of the Deity to believe that He created a few original forms capable of self-development into other and needful forms, as to believe that He required a fresh act of creation to supply the voids caused by the action of His laws." Darwin, without revealing the author's name, included this in later editions of the *Origin*. Later Kingsley wrote his enchanting *Water Babies,* which put the doctrine of evolution into a fairy tale.

This support from one of the clergy was a comfort to Darwin because even Lyell could not go all the way with Darwinism. Henslow and his brother-in-law, Jenyns were, of course, disturbed and yet they had to accept—up to a point—the arguments for evolution.

Other scientists, many of them strangers, wrote Darwin warm letters. But the battle of giants was in preparation and, as the letters piled up and the reviews appeared, Darwin, who folded up like the sensitive plant at criticism, had his bad moments. His old teacher and companion in geologizing, Adam Sedgwick, wrote, "I have read your book with more pain than pleasure . . . parts I read with absolute sorrow, because I think them utterly false and grievously mischievous."

Another embittered friend was Richard Owen, who had written the section on fossil mammals for Darwin's enlarged book on the *Beagle* voyage. Enthusiastic then over Darwin's specimens, he now viciously attacked the theory based on the evidence of those very specimens. Professor Whewell, an old Cambridge friend, refused to have a copy of the *Origin* in the Trinity College Library; Louis Agassiz, the Swiss-born naturalist now at Harvard, fought tooth and nail with Asa Gray against Darwinism. The eminent Sir John Herschel called the *Origin* the book with the "law of higgledy-piggledy." Carlyle snarled and Cardinal Manning got out his cat-o-nine-tails.

Some of the reviews that soon appeared were rabid, some merely stunned, and a few full of high praise. Thomas Huxley, knowing how sensitive his friend was to criticism, wrote him before the storm broke.

I trust you will not allow yourself to be in any way disgusted or annoyed by the considerable abuse and misrepresentation which, unless I greatly mistake, is in store for you. Depend upon it you have earned the lasting gratitude of all thoughtful men. And as to the curs which will bark and yelp, you must recollect that some of your friends, at any rate, are endowed with an amount of combativeness which (though you have often and justly rebuked it) may stand you in good stead. I am sharpening up my claws and beak in readiness.

Luckily, Huxley was not just trying to cheer him up.

Darwin's champion in one of the most dramatic struggles in the history of science had prepared for the battle by early experiences rather like those of the Sage of Down House. Thomas Henry Huxley was born in 1825 at Ealing, near London. His father was master of a small school which Tom attended until he was about ten, when the family moved to Coventry. This ended his formal schooling, but Tom soon began a course of amazingly rapid and serious reading which was to make him one of the most learned men of his period. Before dawn, he would light his candle, pin a blanket around his shoulders, and absorb some scientific work.

Two of his sisters were married to doctors and, despite an early shock at seeing cadavers in the dissecting room, he drifted into medicine. He became apprentice to a doctor working in the slums of east London, where he acquired a flaming hatred of poverty. By accident, he saw a notice in the library of the College of Surgeons of a competition for medals in botany. For months, he neglected sleep to cram for the examination and was overjoyed to receive second prize. Soon after that he won a scholarship for study in Charing Cross Hospital and there he learned the scientific method. At nineteen, he made his first original discovery, the membrane at the root of human hair, still called Huxley's Layer.

After three years at the hospital, Huxley won his degree as Bachelor of Medicine and got a post as assistant surgeon on the *Rattlesnake,* a Navy frigate sent to chart the waters of northeastern Australia. For four years, he had the invaluable experience of field work, like Darwin and Wallace. Working in a corner of the chart room, he concentrated on the study of invertebrates: jellyfish, mollusks, and sea worms. The vast aquariums of the Indian and South Pacific Oceans offered myriads of creatures, many of them transparent, revealing their secrets without the need of dissection. He sent papers on his invertebrates to the Royal Society, meanwhile exploring other fields—histology, zoology, geology, and physiology.

Like Darwin, he returned home to find a reputation waiting for him. He was elected a Fellow of the Royal Society and, a year later, received its medal. In 1854, he was appointed professor of natural history and paleontology in the Government School of Mines and, a year later, married Netty Heathorn, whom he had met in Sidney. It was a case of love at first sight—and forever. One of Huxley's letters of congratulations came from his new friend, Charles Darwin, who wrote, "I hope your marriage will not make you idle. Happiness, I fear, is not good for work." An odd remark, which did not apply to either man.

Huxley was, in fact, a dynamo. He fulfilled his private pledge "to give a nobler tone to science" by making contributions in many branches. A great humanitarian, he lectured to workingmen on the wonders of natural history; he learned to lecture and to write brilliantly.

In the years before the publication of *Origin*, Darwin's respect and affection for the younger man developed rapidly and the Huxleys were often guests at Down House. As he wrote his book, Darwin kept Huxley in mind along with Lyell and Hooker as the three men he wanted most to convince. He succeeded in that but he never dreamed that Huxley would care so much about another man's work that he would gladly drop his own to defend it.

By spring, the second large edition of the *Origin* had reached the general public, making the greatest sensation of any scientific book so far published. Despite his hostility, Owen told a committee of Parliament that "the whole intellectual world this year has been excited by a book on the origin of species." He added that visitors were besieging the British Museum, asking to be shown exhibits that would help to explain the mystery of the origin of species. It was probably Owen who wrote an unsigned review of Darwin's book in the *Edinburgh Review*. "It is extremely malignant, clever, and I fear will be very damaging," Darwin lamented to Lyell. And it must have been Sedgwick who wrote an abusive review in the *Spectator*.

Here, Huxley had a chance to use his freshly-sharpened claws. A staff writer on the *London Times* had been assigned the book to review and, since he knew nothing of science, the job was quietly turned over to Huxley. He wrote a magnificient three-column essay on the Darwinian thesis, which, he said, was the best yet offered to explain the development of living forms. Darwin instantly guessed the author. Huxley, whom Darwin's inner circle called Bulldog, wrote several other reviews and lectured on the origin of species at the Royal Institution, with the author himself in the audience. "His mind is as quick as a flash of lightning and as sharp as a razor," Darwin said of his Bulldog. "He is the best talker whom I have ever known."

Unfortunately, Darwin was ill and taking a water cure, when the most dramatic of Huxley's battles in his behalf took place. Late in June, 1860, the British Association held a three day meeting in Oxford and, by the second day, everybody was ignoring the set program and talking about Darwinism. Henslow was chairman and Hooker and Huxley were both on the platform. Professor Owen, who was really virulent in his crusade against Darwin, made an attack on him and Huxley denied all his arguments so effectively that Owen vanished from Oxford. The word got around that Owen had arranged with Samuel Wilberforce, Bishop of Oxford, to attend the meeting the next day and demolish Charles Darwin. The Church was entering the battle against science.

Such crowds appeared to see the jousting that the meeting

was moved to the Library, where about seven hundred people crowded in, many standing, the ladies perched on the window ledges, all aquiver. Again Henslow was chairman and Hooker and Huxley sat on the platform. Everybody dozed through a long disquisition on Darwin by an American professor and woke up when the Bishop pushed his way through the crowd.

Wilberforce spoke, said an eyewitness, "for full half-an-hour with inimitable spirit, emptiness, and unfairness. . . . In a light, scoffing tone, florid and fluent, he assured us there was nothing in the idea of evolution; rock-pigeons were what rock-pigeons had always been." He ridiculed both Darwin and Huxley and ended by turning to Huxley with a sarcastic smile, asking whether it was through his grandfather or grandmother that he claimed descent from a monkey.

Huxley whispered to Hooker, "The Lord hath delivered him into mine hands." Chairman Henslow, trying to quiet the cries from all sides, "Huxley, Huxley," called on him to speak.

"I am here only in the interests of science," he began rather tensely, "and I have not heard anything which can prejudice the case of my august client." He went on with brilliant clarity to declare why Darwin's explanation of the development of species was sound and why the Bishop was incompetent to discuss it. Then he was ready to answer Wilberforce's question about his ancestry.

If there were an ancestor whom I should feel shame in recalling, it would be a *man,* a man of restless and versatile intellect, who, not content with success in his own sphere of activity, plunges into scientific questions with which he has no real acquaintance, only to obscure them by an aimless rhetoric, and distract the attention of his hearers from the real point at issue by eloquent digressions, and skilled appeals to religious prejudice.

The Library rang to its glass roof with pandemonium. The Bishop's supporters, massed in the center of the room, roared furious protests at this attack on the great churchman. Lady Brewster fainted on her window ledge and had to be carried out. The undergraduates loudly rejoiced in this man who had declared he would rather have an ape for an ancestor than Samuel Wilberforce.

There had to be an anticlimax. Robert Fitzroy, now an Admiral and a man of considerable distinction in the new science of weather prediction, had come to the meeting out of a desire to dissociate himself publicly from his former naturalist. His nerves had gotten worse during the years and he later committed suicide. Now he was in one of his famous rages and he proceeded to have hysterics, denouncing Huxley, describing his horror at the *Origin,* and claiming that he had often protested to Darwin about his views. Waving a Bible high over his head, he shouted that this was unimpeachable authority.

The audience cried him down and he subsided. Gradually the meeting, too, quieted and Hooker was given the last word. He asserted in a letter to Darwin that he had smashed . . .

that Amalekite Sam . . . I hit him in the wind at the first shot in ten words taken from his own ugly mouth; and then proceeded to demonstrate (1) that he could never have read your book, and (2) that he was absolutely ignorant of the rudiments of Bot. Science. . . . Sam was shut up—had not a word to say in reply, and the meeting *was dissolved forthwith,* leaving you master of the field after four hours' battle.

16

The Long Harvest

THE YEARS FOLLOWING the publication of his great book were fruitful ones for Charles Darwin. He went peacefully ahead with his work and let his friends battle in the public arena. He had prepared his brief for evolution and had no desire to plead his own case. Since Hooker, Lyell, Gray, and above all Huxley seemed to enjoy their plunge into the greatest scientific battle of the century, and since they were far more effective than he could be in open combat, he felt that he would be most useful in his study at Down House. He had only begun to open up his vast store of evidence for evolution.

He was still preoccupied with evidence because he had collected so much of it and because he felt he could not venture to overthrow established ideas without good reason. He was an extremely conscientious man and he had the humility which goes with greatness and great learning. The hundred years after 1859 have often been called the Century of Darwin, not only because of the importance of his theory, but also because of his influence on scientists in many fields. Darwin had shown scientists how to work, from modest facts to grand theory; he freed the minds of honest people everywhere from old prejudices and half-truths. As a modern botanist expressed his influence, "Darwin cut the leash and the human mind leaped ahead."

Immediately after the *Origin* was published, Darwin set to work to write it all over again, this time including what had been left out of his "abstract." He thought of a three volume work.

By June, 1860, what had been compressed into the first chapter of the *Origin,* variation under domestication, had expanded enough to fill a volume. This made the task of finishing his "big book" so staggering that as the years passed, he simply wrote parts of it and published them as they were finished.

He put aside "Domestication" to watch a plant eat an animal. With his ailing daughter Henrietta, he was visiting one of the Wedgwoods near Ashdown Forest and here he discovered that the sundew, *Drosera,* trapped and devoured insects. Darwin was enraptured. He was soon declaring that he cared more about *Drosera* than the origin of all the species in the world. He carried some of the plants home and experimented with them. If an insect lighted on *Drosera,* its trap-leaves folded around the victim like tentacles. If Darwin touched the leaves with a needle, nothing happened.

"He treats *Drosera* just like a living creature," Emma commented to Lady Lyell, "and I suppose he hopes to end in proving it an animal." Darwin himself joked about this "disguised animal."

By now, he knew that the trapped insect was eaten by *Drosera.* He found that this remarkable plant had a digestive fluid like that in animals and that the leaves would respond when he put them in water containing bits of meat and egg white, but did not react to plain water.

The insect eaters were now a hobby for holiday prowls and, in 1875, he published a book on this delightful subject, *Insectivorous Plants*. Meanwhile there were orchids. Down House was in the center of a wild orchid country and friends scattered over the globe sent exotics. By now Darwin had a hothouse down in the garden and he enjoyed his work with these exquisite flowers so much that he sometimes felt guilty. "I never was more interested in any subject in all my life than this of orchids," he confessed to Hooker.

A collector in Madagascar sent him the Star of Bethlehem, a variety with a nectar tube nearly a foot long. The nectar filled only the bottom inch or so. That meant that only an insect with a proboscis ten or eleven inches long could get at the nectar. The experts assured Darwin that no such insect existed. But he was sure that this orchid depended on an insect for fertilization. This was perfectly plain when he inserted a fine rod down into the nectary and it came up bearing a clump of pollen. It was impossible for the insect to drink the nectar without brushing against the anthers with their sticky crowns of pollen.

A little later an insect was discovered, a moth with a coiled proboscis. Unrolled, it was long enough to reach into the nectary of the Star of Bethlehem and Darwin could write Q.E.D.

Then there was the Catasetum orchid, sent by a botanist on Trinidad. This fascinating creature had a different mechanism for tricking insects into carrying pollen. When a bee lighted on a male flower, a tiny sensitive spring was released and a mass of pollen shot out from the anthers, striking the visiting bee on the back. "Happy man," Darwin wrote Asa Gray, "he who has actually seen crowds of bees flying round Catasetum, with the pollonia sticking to their backs!" The bees in their rounds would visit a female flower and rub off the pollen on its stigma, the sticky crown of the seedmaking part.

Darwin tried out the pollen-firing mechanism, a "truly marvellous" device. He held the flower a few feet from his study window and lightly touched the long, prong-like trigger in imitation of an insect. The pollen mass exploded and struck the window pane, where it remained cemented with its own "glue." Dissecting this trigger organ, he studied its structure and experimented with a device made on the same principle. He cut a tiny strip of whalebone, weighted at one end, and bent it around a small cylinder. With the head of a pin, he gently held down the upper end. Then as he let go, the whalebone, just like the pollinium, shot forward carrying its weighted end.

Darwin studied with the same care the intricate contrivances by which certain orchids kept their pollen from touching their own stigmas. This insured cross-fertilization, which produced a sturdier progeny. His book, *The Fertilization of Orchids,* came out in 1862 and was an enormous success.

With equal absorption, he studied the movements of climbing plants, perplexed by the twining of their tendrils and stems. "Some of the adaptations displayed by climbing plants are as beautiful as those of orchids for ensuring cross-fertilization," he wrote. He discovered that the movement of the buds is always upward, while their stems and tendrils turn downward. *The Power of Movement in Plants* completed his trilogy of botanical oddities.

When time and health allowed, Darwin toiled over his *Variation of Animals and Plants under Domestication.* This book, more than twice as long as the *Origin,* expanded its first chapter on variations in horses, pigs, cattle, sheep, pigeons, cats and dogs, trees and grain which were deliberately produced by breeding. Wading through books on history, art, and literature, and breeders' journals, and adding data from his own experience, he traced these domestic forms to their wild ancestors. By conscious selection, man had produced fleet race horses, cattle with increased weight and early maturity, the setter dog, the fleshy gooseberry, and full-grained wheatstalks. By "slow and insensible changes," the desired variations were transmitted, while the unwanted ones disappeared.

The book was published in 1868 and, despite its "horrid, disgusting bigness," it had a favorable reception. Its first edition of 2750 copies sold out soon after printing. A grudging, patronizing review in the *Athenaeum* said:

> On the "Origin of Species" Mr. Darwin has nothing, and is never likely to have anything, to say; but on the vastly important subject of inheritance, the transmission of peculiarities once acquired through successive generations, this work is a valuable store-house of facts for curious students and practical breeders.

Darwin now turned to his notes on the origin of man. As usual, he contemplated a small volume; in fact, man was to have been included in *Animals and Plants* but was crowded out. For Darwin, the development of man was part of the grand and continuous process of evolution from lower forms. "Convinced that species are mutable productions, I could not avoid the belief that man must come under the same law," he wrote.

But as late as 1857, he had written Wallace that he would avoid a subject as "surrounded with prejudices" as the descent of man. Even those close to him, Lyell for instance, wrote guardedly on the subject. Wallace also wavered on the matter of man's origin. But Darwin was determined that "no honourable man should accuse" him of concealing his views. And so, early in 1868, he got to work in earnest.

"He who wishes to decide whether man is the modified descendant of some pre-existing form, would probably first enquire whether man varies, however slightly, in bodily structure and in mental faculties . . ." he began in *The Descent of Man.*

It is well-known, he went on, that man is built on the same general model as other mammals. All his bones, muscles, nerves, blood vessels, and internal organs could be compared with the corresponding ones in a monkey, bat, or seal. Even the brain shows the same major folds and fissures. Man is subject to some of the same diseases as lower animals. The very similarity of the tissues and blood, as seen under the microscope and by chemical analysis, points to a relationship.

Then there is the evidence from reproduction. Man, like other animals, develops from a tiny ovule which apparently differs in no important respect from the ovules of other animals. The embryos of man and animal in their early stages of development can hardly be distinguished from each other. Illustrating this point with pictures of human and dog embryos at the same stage of development, Darwin revealed their similarity. At certain stages, the human embryo has gill slits like the fish and the tail and hairy covering of other mammals.

Man, like other animals, has rudimentary or leftover parts: wisdom teeth, appendix, muscles that wiggle the ear —all no longer useful. The ruminants or cud-chewers have grinding teeth but never develop incisors. Man differs from other primates in being born almost naked, but with a few short, straggling body hairs as rudiments of the hairy coat of lower animals.

Variation between individuals, so universal in living

forms, is also found in man. Who can deny that no two individuals are exactly alike, that they in fact differ in hundreds of ways? And if variation exists, then why should not natural selection have operated in the case of some primitive ancestor?

How did man come to occupy a dominant position and achieve his immense superiority over lower forms by virtue of his mental faculties? Perhaps some favorable variation enabled a primitive ancestor to leave the safety of the trees for the more plentiful food supply on the ground. Here, it would have been to his advantage to become a biped and walk on two legs. His two freed limbs, no longer necessary for walking, must have become useful for grasping and eventually for handling tools. Those apes which most easily learned to walk upright had the best chance of survival.

Here, Darwin came to his most difficult problem, the enormous gap between the mentality of man and ape. He didn't flinch. To be sure, the difference between the highest ape and the lowest savage was enormous, but so was the difference between the Fuegian savage and a Newton or a Shakespeare. The difference was one of degree.

In their own way, animals experience emotions: fear, pain, pleasure, terror, happiness, misery, and even sympathy with each other in distress or danger. Even language is not altogether absent in animals. By his bark, a dog can express a great variety of feelings.

We should admit the community of descent, Darwin argued. "It is only our natural prejudice, and that arrogance which made our forefathers declare that they were descended from demi-gods, which leads us to demur to this conclusion." He felt it was more heartening to think that man has risen from a low state to high standards of knowledge, morals, and religion. And he ended on this note:

Man may be excused for feeling pride at having risen . . . to the very summit of the organic scale; and the fact of having thus risen, instead of having been ab-originally placed there, may give him hope for a still higher destiny in the distant future.

The Descent of Man, Darwin's second great book, was published in February, 1871 and two printings, totalling 7500 copies, were made that year. Darwin received 1470 pounds for this first edition, a huge royalty for those days. He was now revising the *Origin* for a sixth edition and translations were out in Germany, France, Russia, Holland, Italy, and Sweden. In the dozen years since it had turned the British scientific world upside down, the public had come to accept evolution and its author more quietly.

For this reason, there was less uproar about the *Descent of Man,* though it brought evolution far too close for comfort. The July issue of the *Edinburgh Review* probably described its reception accurately, "On every side it is raising a storm of mingled wrath, wonder and admiration." But James Hague, an American visiting Darwin just after the book came out, remarked, "everybody is talking about it without being shocked." And Huxley, who might well take much of the credit for the changed attitude, wrote, "As time has slipped by, a happy change has come over Mr. Darwin's critics. The mixture of ignorance and insolence, which at first characterized a large proportion of the attacks with which he was assailed, is no longer the sad distinction of anti-Darwinian criticism."

By now the Sage of Down was beginning to look like Merlin—or perhaps it was the other way about. Illustrators of Tennyson's *Idylls of the King* may have made Merlin look like Darwin. The beard, which he had been letting grow for several years, was getting longer and whiter and his hair had retreated to expose the remarkable high dome of his forehead. His bristling eyebrows fairly jutted now over his brooding gray eyes. He had the scholar's stoop but he still was taller than most men—and every inch a genius. There was a mysterious quality about him that seemed to go with medieval alembics and potions but his particular brand of magic really belonged to the twentieth century.

At Down there was still the schedule of work and rest, the sandwalk, and the two evening games of backgammon with Emma. When Charles lost, he would cry, "Bang your bones!" (an expression he had picked up from Swift's *Journal to Stella*). But by dint of keeping records, he proved that Emma lost oftener. Writing to Asa Gray, he crowed, "Pray give our regards to Mrs. Gray. I know she likes to hear men boasting, it refreshes them so much. Now the tally with my wife in backgammon stands thus: she, poor creature, has won only 2490 games, whilst I have won, hurrah, hurrah, 2795 games!"

The children had grown up. That summer of 1871, Henrietta married Richard Litchfield, a barrister and one of the founders of the Workingmen's College. They were to live in London and soon Darwin wrote his daughter plaintively, "Well, it is an awful and astounding fact that you are married, and I shall miss you sadly." But he added that Litchfield would come to worship her as he worshiped Emma, "our dear old mother."

The other daughter, Elizabeth, could never be tempted away from Down but one by one the sons went out into the world. Francis, William, and Horace married and moved away; Leonard went in for an army career; William became a banker in Southhampton. Horace and George were at Cambridge; Horace beginning his career as a maker of scientific instruments and George well along in his work as a brilliant astronomer. Darwin had gone down to Cambridge in 1870 to visit his sons, missing Henslow who was now dead, but having a warm reception from old Adam Sedgwick who had recovered from his rage at the *Origin.*

Charles and Emma went to London now and then to visit the children and Erasmus, and the friends who still belonged to the inner circle: Lyells, Hookers, and Huxleys. Their happiness lay in their small intimate world of family and friends but they took a benevolent interest in village affairs. Darwin was Treasurer of the Coal Club and served for some years as county magistrate. As his vicar said, Darwin's "liberal contribution was ever ready." As quietly as possible he helped out promising young scientists or older ones who were pinched for money. Most public issues and events did not touch him closely, but he was tremendously aroused by the Civil War in the United States and rejoiced when the Union was preserved and slavery abolished. And when the issue of vivisection came up in Parliament, Darwin, the soul of tenderness to animals, testified before the Royal Commission on the necessity of animal experiments for the saving of human lives. In his hierarchy of species, man was most precious.

On the heels of the *Descent of Man* came his psychological study, *Expression of the Emotions in Man and Animals.* He had made his first notes for this book when his first-born, Mr. Hoddy Doddy, has displayed his feelings by contorting his face in rage or grinning in flattering recognition of his parents. Now William was in his early thirties!

Darwin declared that he felt old and weary and would do no more theorizing. As he entered his last decade, he feared that his mental powers might decline along with what little strength was left him. But those final years proved to be happy and fruitful, his health was better and no blight touched his mind.

Botany was a happy occupation for Darwin during the 1870's and he also completed his books on plant movements and insect eaters, flower forms and fertilization.

In 1876, Francis lost his wife and came home to Down with his infant son, Bernard. This first grandchild was a constant joy and Frank, as the family called him, stayed close at his father's side as secretary and collaborator. He had trained as a physician but readily became a botanist.

Writing to George to congratulate him on the papers he was to present before the Royal Society, Darwin said:

> I know I shall feel quite proud. . . . Horace goes on Monday to lecture on his dynam. at Birmingham. Frank is getting on very well with Dipsacus and has now made experiments which convince me that the matter which comes out of the gland is real live pro-toplasm, about which I was beginning to feel horrid doubts. Leonard is going to build forts—Oh Lord, what a set of sons I have, all doing wonders.

All his sons were indeed to achieve distinction in their careers: George, Francis, and Horace were honored with knighthood; Leonard was President of the Eugenics Society and the Royal Geographical Society; and Francis, President of the British Association for the Advancement of Science.

Darwin's devotion to his sons extended to their wives. When William, at the age of thirty-eight became engaged to Sara Sedgwick of a distinguished New England family, Charles welcomed her into the family with a warm letter. "I must tell you how deeply I rejoice over my son's good fortune," he wrote. "You will believe me, when I say that for very many years I have not seen any woman, whom I have liked and esteemed as much as you."

The Darwin-Wedgwood gift for deep family affection had not diminished since the days at Maer. As part of his clan feeling, Darwin in these last years was impelled to write an informal autobiography for his children and grandchildren, and then a memoir of his grandfather, Erasmus, the family pioneer in the field of evolution.

Research continued to be the delight of Charles Darwin's ever inquiring mind. He returned to one of his earliest hobbies, the earthworm. He studied its reaction to light and sound. These creatures were not disturbed at their nightly labors by a low diffused light but took alarm when he held a lighted candle close to them. They ignored the sounds of whistle or horn but were sensitive to low vibrations and scurried off to their burrows when he struck low C on the piano. In the field, he measured their tremendous collective work of turning up the soil, preparing it for the growth of crops. He well remembered the sterile lands in South America, sour and useless without the unending stirring and sifting of soil by worms.

His last book, *The Formation of Vegetable Mould, through the Action of Worms,* was published in 1881. He was surprised at the "almost laughable enthusiasm" which greeted the book but his tribute to these lowly creatures is a biological and agricultural classic.

Except for the Royal Society's Copley Medal which Darwin received in 1865, official honors came late. When they poured in during the 1870's, it was a sign that tempers in high scientific places had simmered down. Throughout the world, he was made an honorable member of scientific societies. The French Institute hesitated until 1878 and then admitted him not to the zoological section but to the botanical. This amused Darwin, who claimed, of course with complete inaccuracy, that his knowledge of botany amounted to recognizing that a daisy was a composite and a pea a legume.

In 1877, his alma mater gave him an LL.D. degree, a

momentous occasion for the Darwins and the annals of Cambridge. In the traditional scarlet robe, Darwin appeared on the platform of the Senate House to the lusty cheers of the undergraduates crowded into the gallery.

Emma, who was there with her daughter Bessy and four of her sons, described the occasion in a letter to William. "I thought he would be overcome," she reported of her famous husband, "but he was quite stout and smiling and sat for a considerable time waiting for the Vice-Chancellor." However, there was no lack of entertainment in the interval, for the undergraduates had smuggled in a monkey. It soon appeared, dangling on a string, crossing the hall from one gallery to the other. A proctor was foolish enough to capture it, Emma wrote, and soon it was followed by a ring tied with ribbons, which was evidently the "Missing Link."

The ceremony which followed was all dignity and then the family lunched in George's rooms. Darwin did not feel equal to staying for the great dinner to be given in his honor by the Philosophical Club and went home to Down.

Once more Huxley deputized for his beloved friend, responding to a toast with a mixture of satire and seriousness. He reminded the gathering that Cambridge had waited to shower her honors on Darwin until it was "safe and superfluous." Then he paid his own tribute: "From Aristotle's great summary of the biological knowledge of his time down to the present, there is nothing comparable to the *Origin of Species* as a connected survey of the phenomena of life permeated and vivified by a central idea."

During the winter of 1881, Darwin's strength began to fail and he had attacks of faintness and pains in the chest. He gave up his daily excursion with the terrier, Polly, around the sandwalk. There had been deep losses of late —his beloved Lyell, Cousin Josiah Wedgwood, and then his brother Erasmus, buried in Downe churchyard. But on a visit to Cambridge in October, he had spent a happy week with Horace and his wife, whose first child was born that December—another Erasmus. Five generations—and a cycle was closed around that wonderful old figure hobnobbing with his fellow Lunatics, Watts and Priestley and the first Josiah Wedgwood, and the unknown quantity, the new Erasmus Darwin, squalling or cooing in Cambridge.

His own years made their full circle now and on April 19, 1882, Charles Darwin died peacefully, surrounded by his loved ones.

All England mourned with them and all around the world the collectors of orchids and beetles who cherished his letters, and the men of learning who had spent happy days at Down, and the younger scientists who were working at researches inspired from some hint in his books, felt their personal loss. The London *Times*, which had caused Darwin hours of chagrin in the past, now said he was "beyond rivalry among the men of today and side by side with two or three great discoverers of the past."

Darwin had wished to be buried at Downe beside his brother. But Parliament desired to give him the greatest final honor possible, burial in Westminster Abbey.

On April 26, there was a distinguished gathering in the Abbey of the nation's great in science, politics, and the arts, along with representatives from America and the countries of Europe. The two Darwin daughters and the five sons were there but Emma remained at Down.

The pallbearers were Hooker, Huxley, Wallace, and others not so much friends as symbols: James Russell Lowell, the Minister of the United States; the President of the Royal Society; two dukes; and an earl. As they brought the wreath covered coffin to be placed in a vault beside Newton's the choir chanted:

"Happy is the man who findeth wisdom and the man that getteth understanding."

Index

Aconcaqua, 96
Adventure H. M. S., 84, 93, 98
Agassiz, Louis, 30, 168
Albermarle Island, 110
Andes, 45, 90-92, 96, 103, 105
Argentina, 88, 98
Argentine pampas, 73, 85, 86, 88
atolls, 115-116
Audubon, John, 34, 35
Australia, 113
Autobiography, 32, 38

Bahia, 64-66, 72, 113
Bahia Blanca, 87
Banks, Joseph, 80
Bates, Henry Walter, 149
Beagle H. M. S., 13, 14, 44-49,
    50-54, 56, 61, 72, 73, 78-
    116
Brazil, 61, 64-73, 95
Buenos Aires, 78, 84
Butler, Samuel, 22, 24, 77

Butler School, 23
Button, Jemmy, 64, 80, 83, 88

Cape Horn, 68, 82, 94
Cape Verde Island, 55-56, 59
Carlyle, Thomas, 123, 168
Charles Island, 111
Chatham Island, 105-106, 109
Chile, 99, 101-104
Chiloe, 99-100
Chonos, 99
Cocos Islands, 113
Concepción, earthquake of, 100-
    101
Cook, Capt. James, 44, 64, 80
Coral Reefs, 132
Cordilleras, 90, 91, 97, 101, 104
Corfield, Richard, 96, 98

Darwin, Anne Elizabeth, 133
    Caroline, 18, 19, 26, 27, 36,
      70, 79, 96, 113, 116, 124

Darwin (*continued*)
Catherine, 18, 19, 21, 27, 125-127, 140
Charles Waring, 139
Elizabeth, 139, 182
Emma (Wedgwood), 26, 27, 36, 121, 125-131, 133, 138-140, 142-144, 182, 186, 187
Erasmus (brother), 18, 22, 24, 30-34, 53, 78, 118, 120, 123, 128, 130, 131, 140, 147, 186
Erasmus (grandfather), 14, 15, 16, 38, 44, 58, 125, 185
Francis, 139-141, 182, 184
George, 139, 182, 184
Henrietta (Litchfield), 139, 175, 182
Horace, 139, 182, 184
Leonard, 139, 144, 182, 184
Marianne, 18, 27, 146
Mary Eleanor, 133, 139
Robert, 14-20, 23, 29, 31, 36, 47, 140
Susan, 18, 26, 27, 42, 140, 147
Susannah (Wedgwood), 17-19, 147
William Erasmus, 131, 182-184, 186
De Candolle, 144
Descent of Man, 179, 181
Down House, 133-147

Ecuador, 105
Endeavor, H. M. S., 80
Entomological Society, 150
Etruria Hall, 17, 18
Etruria Works, 15
Evolution, 33, 58, 77, 93, 102-103, 109-113, 116, 138, 160, 161, 163-165, 179-181

Expression of the Emotions in Man and Animals, 182

Falkland Islands, 84, 88, 90
Fertilization of Orchids, 177
finches, 110-111
Fitzroy, Robert, 44, 48-51, 54, 58, 62, 64, 67, 76, 80, 84, 88, 90, 92-94, 101, 105, 109, 121, 173
fossils, 74, 76, 87, 89, 109, 119, 123, 124, 165
Fox, William, 40, 42, 137, 153
Fuegians, 64, 79-84, 180

Galapagos Islands, 105, 109, 111, 112, 137, 153
Albermarle Is., 110
Charles Is., 111, 112
Chatham Is., 105-106
James Is., 110
Galton, Francis, 125, 126
gauchos, 85-87, 97
guasos, 97, 101
Geological Society, 120, 122, 123
Grant, Robert Edmund, 33, 34, 122
Gray, Asa, 142, 152, 155, 159, 161, 163, 166, 168, 174, 176, 182

Henslow, John Steven, 40, 41, 43, 45, 47, 57, 61, 77, 78, 87, 96, 104, 119, 121, 122, 131, 149, 167, 172
Herschel, Sir John, 42, 131, 168
Hooker, Joseph, 137, 138, 140, 155-157, 163, 166, 170, 172, 174, 187
Humboldt, von Alexander, 42, 43
Hutton, James, 58

Huxley, Thomas Henry, 140, 150-152, 166, 168-173, 186, 187

Insectivorous Plants, 176
Isla Isabella (see Albermarle Is.)

Jameson, Dr. Robert, 35
Jefferson, Thomas, 16, 17
Journal, 79, 84, 96, 110, 111, 123, 125, 131, 136, 137, 139, 149, 151, 153

Lamarck, Jean Baptiste, 33, 58
Linnean Society, 120, 150, 156-157, 159
Lunar Society, 16, 17, 187
Lyell, Charles, 57-59, 76, 88, 94, 101, 102, 115, 119, 121, 123, 125, 128, 131, 137, 140, 147, 151-157, 163, 166, 170, 174, 186

"Mackaw Cottage," 130
Mackintosh, Sir James, 37
    Frances, 120
Maer, 25, 26, 28, 32, 37, 42, 46, 77, 94, 118, 119, 121, 136
Maldonado, 85
Malthus, Thomas Robert, 132, 153, 160
mastodon, 76
Mauritius Is., 113
Megatherium, 74
Montevideo, 78, 84, 85
Mount, 18, 20, 22, 24, 25, 28, 32, 37, 77, 118, 121
Murray, John, 163

New Zealand, 113

Origin of Species, 132, 138, 162, 163, 166, 167, 170, 178, 186
Owen, Fanny, 28, 42
    Richard, 122, 123, 131, 173
    Sarah, 28, 42
Oxford meeting, 171-173

Patagonia, 88-92, 97, 119
Peacock, George, 45
Peru, 104, 105
Peuquenes, 102, 103
Plata La, 86, 87
Plinian Society, 34
Plymouth, 114
Port Famine, 94
Porto Praia, 59
Power of Movement of Plants, 177
Punta Alta, 74, 119, 123

Rio de Janeiro, 69, 70
Rio Negro, 86
Rio de la Plata, 84
Royal Medical Society, 34

Samerang H. M. S., 67
San Cristobal, (see Chatham Is.)
San Salvador, (see James Is.)
Santa Cruz River, 90-92
Santa Maria, (see Charles Is.)
Sedgwick, Adam, 41, 43, 44, 77, 119, 122, 168, 173
Severn River, 20, 28
Shrewsbury, 19, 20, 24, 30, 96, 117, 118, 136, 146
Shrewsbury Bell Stone, 30
Smith, William, 58
South Pacific, 45, 113-114
St. Jago, 59, 61, 136

Tahiti, 113
Tierra del Fuego, 14, 15, 78, 84, 88, 90, 92, 119
Teneriffe, 14, 43, 45, 54, 55, 59, 96, 119

Uruguay, 73, 87
Uspallata Pass, 103

Valdivia, 99, 100, 101
Valparaiso, 95-99, 104
Variations of Animals and Plants under Domestication, 177
Volcanic Is., 136

Wallace, Alfred Russel, 148-158, 162, 163, 178, 187
Wedgwood, Elizabeth, 25-27, 121, 146
  Hensleigh, 120, 123, 131
  Josiah, 14, 17, 25, 94, 118, 121, 123, 127
Wernerian Society, 34
Wilberforce, Bishop Samuel, 171

Zoological Society, 120, 123, 150
Zoonomia, 16, 23

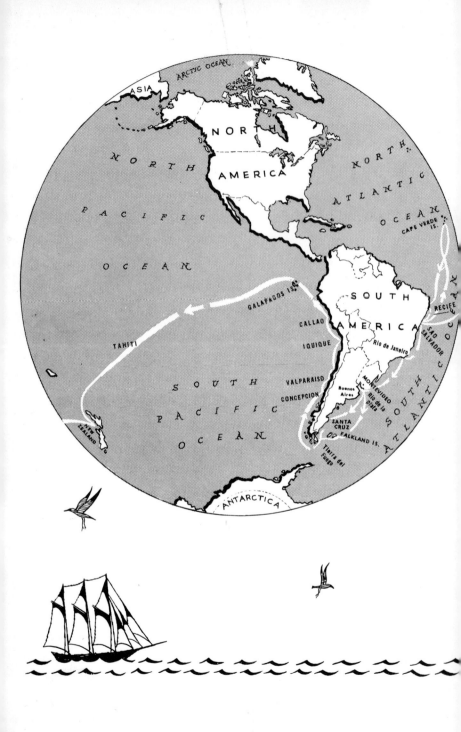